gateway science

G000037878

HIGHER

revision guide

OCR Science

for GCSE

Elaine Gill • David Lees • Pauline Anning

Series editor: Bob McDuell

Heinemann

From Harcourt

Heinemann Educational Publishers
Halley Court, Jordan Hill, Oxford OX2 8EJ
Part of Harcourt Education

Heinemann is the registered trademark of Harcourt Education Limited

© Harcourt Education Limited 2007

First published 2007

11 10 09 08 07
10 9 8 7 6 5 4 3 2

British Library Cataloguing in Publication Data is available from the British Library on request.

ISBN: 978 0 435675 44 8

Designed by Wooden Ark
Project managed, edited and typeset by Bookcraft Ltd (Alex Sharpe, Project Manager; Peter Millward, Editor)

Harcourt project team: David Cooke, Andrew Halcro-Johnston, Sarah Ross, Ruth Simms, Iti Singh, Peter Stratton

Original illustrations © Harcourt Education Limited 2007

Illustrated by Bookcraft India Pvt Ltd (Gemma Raj), HL Studios

Printed and bound in China through Phoenix Offset

Cover photo © Getty Images

Every effort has been made to contact copyright holders of material reproduced in this book. Any omissions will be rectified in subsequent printings if notice is given to the publishers.

About this book

This OCR Gateway Science revision guide will help you revise for the OCR Gateway higher exams. One exam consists of modules B1, C1 and P1 and the other of B2, C2 and P2. The guide summarises what you have learnt and links directly to the OCR Science specification.

This guide is broken down into the six modules: B1, B2, C1, C2, P1 and P2. Each module covers eight items (a–h), for example B1a–B1h. You will find some items are combined into one section, for example B1a & B1b.

Each section starts with a **learning outcome** which summarises the main points covered. This will help you to focus on what you need to revise in that section.

Key words are shown in bold and you will find them indexed at the back of the guide. **Equations** are highlighted to help you use and apply them.

The exam may ask you to consider ideas about 'How science works'. The **How Science works** boxes will help you apply this thinking to your answers. Remember that you should be continually questioning how scientists collect data, use and interpret evidence.

Exam tips highlight common mistakes and give you advice about exam preparation so you can achieve better grades.

You will find lots of simple, full colour diagrams, including **spider diagrams**, to help with your revision and to make the content more digestible. Try drawing your own spider diagrams to help you remember key concepts.

We have given you **'Test yourself' questions** at the end of each section to help you to check that you have understood the content. Use the **answers** at the back of the guide to check whether you have got them all correct – if not, go back and revise that section again.

The revision guide is based on the new specification and the example **exam-style questions** on page 74 will give you valuable preparation for the exams.

Remember that these questions are for revision and homework. The exams will also contain some recall and one-mark questions. In your revision you should think beyond the basic ideas so that you have a better understanding for the exams.

The **answers** that follow the questions will allow you to check your progress and improve next time.

Good luck with your exams!

Contents

B1a Fit for life & B1b What's for lunch?

After revising these items you should:

- be able to explain blood pressure, respiration, fitness and diet.

Heart and blood pressure

Exercise increases blood pressure. If you have your blood pressure taken when you visit the doctor or hospital, you are given two numbers.

- The first number is the **systolic** pressure.
- The second usually a lower number, is the **diastolic** pressure.

Blood pressure is measured in millimetres of mercury (mm Hg).

The table shows normal, high and low blood pressures.

Blood pressure	Systolic (mm Hg)	Diastolic (mm Hg)
normal	130	75
high	160	105
low	90	40

High blood pressure can cause:

- weak blood vessels to burst • strokes
- kidney damage • damage to the brain.

Low blood pressure can cause:

- poor circulation • dizziness • fainting.

Blood pressure varies with age and lifestyle:

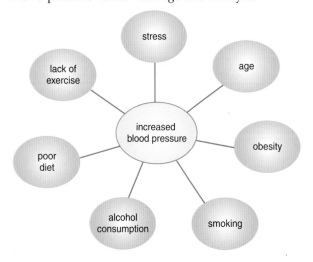

How science works

We can collect data about the blood pressure and lifestyle of many people. This data is analysed and conclusions drawn.

As a result, suggestions can be made to those with high or low blood pressure on how to change their lifestyle to try to keep their blood pressure within normal ranges.

For example, those who are obese with high blood pressure could be advised to lose weight. This should bring their blood pressure down.

Fitness

The time it takes for your pulse rate to get back to normal is one way of measuring fitness. Fitness is the ability of your body to carry out physical exercise. This is not the same as being healthy or disease free. Fitness can also be assessed by measuring:

- stamina • agility • flexibility
- speed • strength
- cardiovascular efficiency.

How science works

You can measure a person's fitness in several different ways. You can measure strength by seeing how many press ups they can do. You can measure recovery rate by calculating how long it takes for their pulse rate to return to normal. The data can be evaluated and its validity and reliability assessed.

Respiration

Every cell in your body respires all the time. This releases energy from **glucose**, which enables you to carry out all your daily activities. There are two types of **respiration**:

- Aerobic – using oxygen.
- Anaerobic – without oxygen.

The word and symbol equations for **aerobic respiration** are:

glucose + oxygen $\rightarrow$ **carbon dioxide** + water + energy

$$C_6H_6O_6 + 6O_2 \rightarrow 6CO_2 + 6H_2O + energy$$

The word equation for **anaerobic respiration** is:

glucose $\longrightarrow$ **lactic acid** + energy

Anaerobic respiration is carried out when the body cannot provide enough oxygen to the cells. This type of respiration does not break down the glucose completely. It produces lactic acid which accumulates in the muscles and causes pain (cramp) and fatigue.

Anaerobic respiration takes place during hard exercise.

- The muscles need more oxygen and glucose to release the energy needed.
- Anaerobic respiration causes an **oxygen debt**, which has to be repaid.
- Therefore extra oxygen is needed when exercise has finished to break down the lactic acid.
- Continued panting replaces oxygen, allowing aerobic respiration.
- The heart beats faster to try to circulate more blood to the muscles.
- The blood also carries lactic acid to the liver where it is broken down.

Anaerobic respiration releases much less energy than aerobic respiration.

If you are running to train for an important sporting event, your pulse rate and breathing rate increase. When you stop, your pulse and breathing rates return to normal. The length of time it takes to return to normal depends on your fitness. A professional athlete's pulse rate returns to normal more quickly than an unfit person's.

Balanced diet

A balanced diet means eating the correct nutrients in the correct quantities. The diet for each person depends on their age, gender and activity.

- If they are doing a manual job they will need more of some nutrients.
- Vegetarians and vegans need a different diet from those who eat meat so that they get all their essential amino acids.
- People with allergies need to avoid certain foods. If you are allergic to peanuts or have a reaction to gluten, then you must avoid food containing these items.
- Some people cannot eat certain foods for religious reasons.

First class **proteins** (from animal protein) contain all the essential amino acids we need. Plant protein only contains some of the amino acids we need. Diets lacking in protein lead to the deficiency disease **kwashiorkor**. This is common in developing countries.

The amount of protein we need each day is called the recommended daily average (RDA) and can be calculated.

RDA (in grams) = body mass (in kilograms) × 0.75

Body mass index

The BMI (body mass index) is used to find out whether people are the right weight or not. Calculate it by measuring your mass in kilograms and your height in metres and use this formula:

$$BMI = \frac{\text{mass in kilograms}}{(\text{height in metres})^2}$$

By using BMI charts, this index tells us whether we are underweight, healthy, overweight or obese.

BMI	State of weight
up to 19	underweight
19–24	healthy weight
25–28	overweight
over 28	obese

Obesity in young people is a major cause for concern. It can lead to many long-term illnesses. The desire for a 'perfect' body can lead to low self-esteem and poor self-image. This can lead to a poor diet.

Digestion

Food is made of large, **insoluble** pieces. It must be broken down into small, soluble molecules. This is done:

- physically – in the mouth by the teeth and in the stomach by squeezing the food
- chemically – in the digestive system with the help of **enzymes**.

The table shows three food groups, the enzymes that help to break them down, where the enzyme is made and what the food is broken down into.

Food group	Enzymes	Where the enzyme is made	Product
protein	protease	stomach small intestine pancreas	amino acids
fat	lipase	pancreas	fatty acids glycerol
carbohydrate	amylase	mouth small intestine	simple sugars

Digestion takes place in our digestive system. Different parts of the digestive system are specialised for different functions.

- Hydrochloric acid is added in the stomach to kill bacteria and to provide the correct pH for the **protease** enzymes.
- **Bile** is added in the small intestine to **emulsify fats**. This improves fat digestion by breaking the fat into smaller pieces. This increases the **surface area** for enzyme action.
- The small molecules are absorbed into the blood plasma or the lymph. This happens in the small intestine by **diffusion**.

Exam tip

You should know the parts of the digestive system and the function of each part.

Work out a mnemonic to help you remember the parts.

Test yourself

1 What changes could someone with high blood pressure make to their lifestyle to bring their blood pressure back to normal?

2 What is the difference in energy output of the two types of respiration?

3 Why does low blood pressure cause fainting?

4 Why do active people need more food than inactive ones?

5 How does the emulsification of fats help digestion?

6 Calculate the BMI of a person who is 1.8 m tall and weighs 80 kg. Which category do they come in: underweight, healthy, overweight or obese?

7 Calculate the RDA for protein for a child who weighs 20 kg and a teenager who weighs 45 kg. Why is there a difference?

B1c Keeping healthy

After revising these items you should:

- understand what makes us ill and what makes us better.

Causes of disease

The diagram shows the causes of disease.

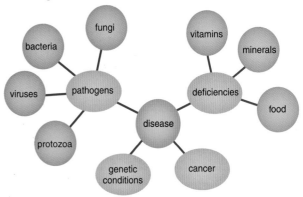

Cancer occurs when cells divide in an uncontrolled way producing a mass called a **tumour**. There are two types of tumour:

- **Benign** – tumours that stop growing.
- **Malignant** – tumours that continue to grow and spread, which makes them dangerous.

We can make changes to our lifestyle to reduce the risk of getting some cancers.

The table shows some of many causes of disease.

Disease	Cause of disease
scurvy	vitamin deficiency
anaemia	mineral deficiency
diabetes	body disorder
red–green **colour blindness**	genetic

Malaria

Facts about malaria:

- Malaria is caused by a **parasite**.
- A parasite is an **organism** that lives on or in another living organism causing it harm.
- The malarial parasite lives in the human blood and liver.
- The parasite is spread by the mosquito.
- The human and the mosquito are **hosts** to the parasite.
- An organism that carries parasites from one organism to another is called a **vector**.

Controlling vectors

Malaria can be prevented by destroying the vectors. This knowledge is expanded in the table.

Method	How this stops the vector spreading disease
open water can be drained	there is nowhere for mosquitoes to lay their eggs
open water can be sprayed with chemicals	kills the mosquito eggs, larvae and pupae
fish can be introduced into ponds	fish eat the mosquito larvae
nets can be placed over beds	stops mosquito biting human
humans can take **drugs**	kills the stage of the mosquito in the human

Antibodies and antigens

Pathogens are microorganisms that cause disease. These microorganisms damage cells in our bodies, or produce **toxins**. Each microorganism has a specific **antigen** on its surface. Our bodies produce specific **antibodies** to each antigen. The antibody attaches itself to the antigen and kills the pathogen.

The diagram shows how antibodies attack antigens.

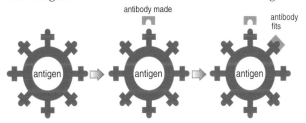

Immunity

There are two types of immunity:

- In **active immunity** we make our own antibodies, copies of which remain in our bodies to be used when another infection occurs.
- In **passive immunity** we have an injection of antibodies made by someone else. This type of immunity does not last long.

Process of immunisation

Immunisation can be done artificially by having an injection of a weakened form of the pathogen (vaccine), which our bodies make antibodies against. If we are ever infected by the live pathogen our bodies are ready to destroy it.

New vaccines continually need to be produced as pathogens keep changing and the antibodies will not work.

Bacterial and fungal infections can be treated by taking **antibiotics**. Over-prescribing and the wrong use of antibiotics have resulted in resistant forms of bacteria evolving. Antibiotics need to be used carefully to prevent the increase of resistant strains of bacteria developing, e.g. MRSA.

The table shows some benefits and risks of immunisation.

Benefits	Risks
we avoid catching diseases	some people have reactions to the vaccines
long-term protection	the weakened viral particles can be passed through the digestive system if taken orally. They pass out in the faeces and could then infect somebody else
eradication of some diseases	

Drug testing

New drugs have to be tested before they can be used to treat humans. This is to ensure they are safe to use. They are tested in several ways.

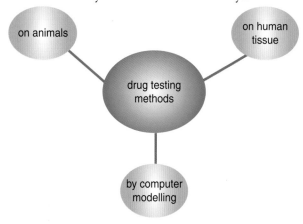

After testing has taken place, the effectiveness of the drugs is assessed by doing blind and double-blind drug trials. Placebos are also used.

Blind trials are when a patient does not know whether they are taking the real drug or a fake. The fake is called a placebo. A double-blind trial is when the doctor also does not know which one the patient is taking.

How science works

Scientists carry out drug testing to ensure the safety and effectiveness of drugs that are eventually prescribed to people. They plan the test, taking great care with the safety aspect, collect the data, analyse the information and evaluate the method and information gained.

Test yourself

1 Look at the pie chart about deaths from cancer in 2004.

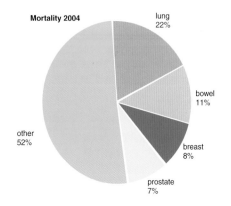

(a) What percentage of the deaths was from lung cancer?
(b) Which cancer was responsible for 8% of deaths?
(c) Which of the cancers named is only found in men?
(d) Suggest other types of cancer.

2 How do the procedures used to prevent malaria work?

3 Why is passive immunity short-lived?

4 What are the objections to the forms of drug testing shown in the diagram opposite?

5 How can you change your lifestyle to reduce the risk of developing cancers?

B1d Keeping in touch

After revising this item you should:

● understand how our bodies communicate.

The eye

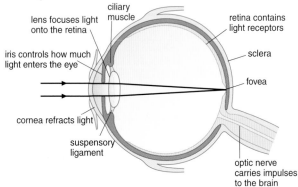

The table shows the functions of parts of the eye.

Part	Function
cornea	refracts light
iris	controls how much light enters the pupil
lens	focuses light onto the retina
retina	contains light **receptors**
optic nerve	carries impulses to the brain

Exam tip

You should know the parts of the eye and their functions.

The position of the two eyes on the head is important. It means you have monocular or binocular vision.

- Monocular vision – the two eyes are on the side of your head. This means you can see all round but you cannot judge distances. This is important for animals that are hunted (**prey** so that they can see **predators**).
- **Binocular vision** – the eyes are on the front of your head. This means you can judge distances but you cannot see all round (without moving your head).

How we see

Light enters the eye from the object. Light is refracted by the cornea and then focused by the lens onto the retina. The ciliary muscles and the suspensory ligament cause the lens to change shape, which allows focusing. This is called accommodation and happens every time we look at objects at different distances from the eye.

Here are some other things you need to know about the eye and vision.

- We have binocular vision. This enables us to judge distances accurately.
- Accommodation does not take place as effectively in older people, so they need reading glasses.
- Colour vision is possible because the retina contains three types of cones which detect red, green and blue light.
- Colour blindness is an inherited condition which means you cannot see colours correctly.

- **Short sight** is caused by the light rays focusing too soon, in front of the retina, because the eyeball is the wrong shape. We can correct this using concave lenses or cornea surgery.

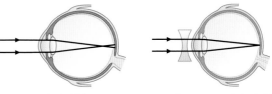

short sight   concave lenses correct short sight

- **Long sight** is caused by the light rays focusing behind the retina. We can correct this using convex lenses.

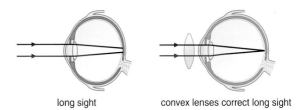

long sight   convex lenses correct long sight

The table shows the causes of eye defects.

Eye defect	Cause of defect
red–green colour blindness	this is inherited from parents and is a lack of specialised cells in the retina
short sight	eyeball or lens is the wrong shape
long sight	eyeball or lens is the wrong shape

The nervous system

The nervous system is made up of individual cells called **neurones**. Neurones are the longest cells in the body – they can be over one metre in length. Nerve impulses are carried in the **axon** of a neurone.

The **sensory** neurones carry information in the form of electrical impulses from the five senses to the central nervous system (CNS). The **motor** neurones carry information from the CNS to the muscles.

Neurones are adapted to their function by:

- length – the impulses can travel to all parts of the body
- having an insulating **sheath** – this keeps the impulse on the right track. It cannot get lost
- having branched endings (**dendrites**) – one neurone can communicate with many others.

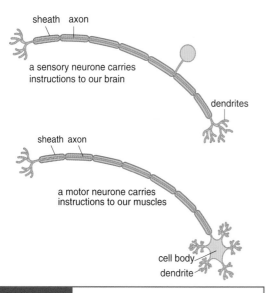

a sensory neurone carries instructions to our brain

a motor neurone carries instructions to our muscles

The junction of two neurones is called a **synapse**.

Facts about synapses:

- The neurones meet at synapses.
- Synapses are tiny gaps.
- The information is passed across the gap by diffusion of chemicals called neuro-**transmitters**.
- The chemical binds with receptor molecules on the membrane of the next neurone.
- This causes a new impulse to be formed.

Reflex arc

The diagram shows a **reflex arc**.

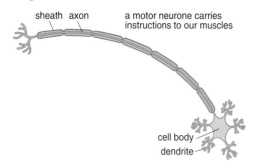

In a reflex arc, there is a set response to a specific stimulus. It always follows this pattern. The table shows this pattern and parts of a spinal reflex pathway.

Pattern	Example
stimulus	pin sticking into your finger
receptor	pain receptor in your skin
sensory neurone	sensory neurone in your arm
CNS	spinal cord
motor neurone	motor neurone in your arm
effector	muscle
response	pull arm away from pin

B1e Drugs and you

Drugs

Drugs are chemicals that produce changes within the body. The table shows the different types of drugs and the effects that they have.

Type of drug	Effect	Example
depressants	slows the brain down	temazepam, alcohol, solvents
stimulants	increases brain activity	nicotine, ecstasy, caffeine
painkillers	reduces pain	aspirin, heroin
performance enhancers	improves athletic performance	anabolic steroids
hallucinogens	changes what we see and hear	LSD, cannabis

Depressants and **stimulants** act on the synapses of the nervous system.

- Depressants slow down transmission across synapses.
- Stimulants speed up transmission across synapses.

Drugs can belong to one or more of these categories:

- legal
- illegal
- social

Legal classification of drugs

The table shows examples of the three classes of drugs.

Class	Example	Other information
A	heroine, cocaine, ecstasy, LSD	possession can lead to seven years in prison
B	amphetamines, barbiturates	possession can lead to five years in prison
C	prescribed drugs, cannabis	possession carries lightest penalties

This classification has consequences both at school, local and national levels. The table shows these arguments.

Arguments for:
People should be free to choose whether they take drugs or not.
Police spend too much time catching drug users.
Legalised drugs would be cheaper and safer for the users.
Cheaper drugs would mean less crime as users try to fund their habit.
Healthworkers would know who the users were and be able to help them kick the habit.
Free hypodermic needles would reduce the risk of drug users reusing them and passing on dangerous diseases such as AIDS.
Arguments against:
Increased drug use may lead to an increase in crime to pay for drugs.
People need to be protected against themselves.
Softer drugs such as cannabis may lead to using harder drugs such as heroin.
Drug use would increase if drugs were legalised.
Drugs affect reaction times. Road accidents and other types of accident would increase.
Cannabis abuse can lead to an increased risk of developing mental illnesses such as psychosis and schizophrenia.

Exam tip

You should know the arguments for and against the legal classification of drugs.

How science works

Decisions made about the classification of drugs affect everybody. Some people think that drugs should be legalised. Others think the opposite. Some people claim that cannabis has some medical uses and want it to be freely available.

Smoking

The table shows some of the substances in cigarettes and cigarette smoke and the effects they have.

Substance	Effects
the drug **nicotine**	nicotine is addictive
tar	tar is an irritant and can cause cancer
tiny particles	these accumulate in the lungs and can lead to bronchitis and emphysema
carbon monoxide	it combines irreversibly with haemoglobin in red blood cells. This prevents oxygen being carried by the red blood cells and may lead to heart disease
other chemicals	these stop the **cilia** from working

The trachea, bronchi and bronchioles are lined with mucus to trap particles and microbes, and cilia which waft the mucus upwards to the back of the throat where it is swallowed. In a smoker, the mucus cannot be removed and builds up.

People cough to try to get rid of this mucus. The mucus can become infected; this is the cause of bronchitis. Sometimes the air sacs are damaged and break down, leading to holes in the lung tissue. This is called emphysema.

Alcohol

Alcohol is a poisonous drug. It is removed from the body by the liver. Drinking too much alcohol over a long period of time can cause damage to the liver (**cirrhosis**), brain and nervous system.

Alcohol consumption is measured in units. The table shows how many units different drinks contain.

Drink	Units
one pint of beer	2
one small glass of wine	1
one measure of spirit, e.g. whisky	1
one small glass of sherry/port	1

This is only a guide as alcoholic drinks have different alcohol contents. The recommended maximum weekly amount is:

* 14 units for women
* 21 units for men.

Alcohol also slows our reaction times. It increases the chance of having an accident whilst driving or operating machinery.

Alcohol level in blood (mg/litre)	Reaction time compared with normal
0.8 the legal limit (two pints of beer)	4x slower
1.2 (3 pints of beer)	15x slower
1.6 (4 pints of beer)	30x slower

How science works

Alcoholic drinks such as wine now have a higher alcohol content than they did 10 years ago. What problem can this cause the drinker and what can governments do?

Some responses could be to give more information about alcohol content, regulations on strength of wines, more breath testing and so on.

Test yourself

1 Name two socially acceptable drugs, two illegal drugs and two legal drugs.

2 What happens to the birth weight of babies born to mothers who smoke during pregnancy?

3 Look at the diagrams of glasses of alcoholic drink.

beer 1 pint	beer ½ pint	wine	spirit
2 units	1 units	1 unit	1 unit

  (a) Anne drinks two glasses of wine and a double gin. How many units of alcohol has she had to drink?

  (b) How many pints of beer does Sanjay drink if he has drunk six units?

  (c) How many units are there in a cocktail containing two spirits and one wine?

4 Why is there a legal limit for the level of alcohol in the blood of drivers?

B1f Staying in balance

After revising this item you should:

* understand how our bodies control their internal environment.

Homeostasis

Homeostasis is the maintenance of a constant internal environment. It involves balancing daily inputs and outputs. It involves negative feedback mechanisms. This is so that cells can function properly. Homeostatic mechanisms enable humans to live in almost every environment on the Earth.

The diagram shows the effect of negative feedback.

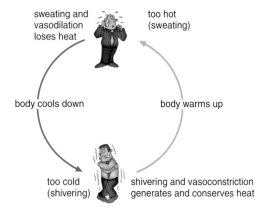

When we are hot, our brain detects the **temperature** of the blood passing through. It sends impulses to the skin so that the capillaries dilate. More blood flows to the skin and we lose heat and cool down. The brain then senses the blood is cooler and impulses are sent to the skin to constrict the capillaries and so less blood flows to the skin. This means less heat is lost. It is a constant monitoring system.

Exam tip

You should know what a negative feedback mechanism is and how it works in homeostasis.

What does the body try to keep constant?

* blood glucose levels
* body temperature at 37°C
* water content   •   carbon dioxide levels.

Controlling body temperature

The skin controls body temperature. The diagram shows a cross-section of the skin and the parts involved in temperature regulation.

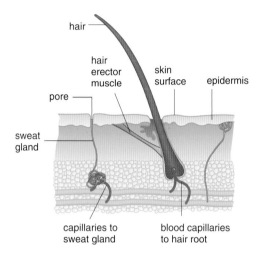

hair

hair erector muscle

skin surface

epidermis

pore

sweat gland

capillaries to sweat gland

blood capillaries to hair root

The body temperature should be maintained at 37°C so that enzymes can work properly. Enzymes are damaged if the temperature is too high and are ineffective if the temperature is too low.
We keep warm by:

- **vasoconstriction** – the blood capillaries in the skin constrict, therefore less blood flows through them so less heat can be lost through the skin
- shivering – the muscles contract, releasing heat which warms us up.

We keep cool by:

- **vasodilation** – the blood capillaries in the skin widen, therefore more blood flows through them so more heat can be lost through the skin
- sweating – sweat is produced on the surface of the skin. Heat from the body is used to evaporate this sweat therefore the body loses its heat to the environment and cools down.

Sex hormones

Sex hormones are responsible for the secondary sexual characteristics that develop at puberty. The table shows the changes that happen to males and females.

Change	Male	Female
voice breaks	✓	x
hair grows on face and body	✓	x
hair grows under the arms	✓	✓
pubic hair grows	✓	✓
more muscular	✓	x
genitals develop	✓	✓
sperm production starts	✓	x
breasts develop	x	✓
hips widen	x	✓
periods start	x	✓

The female hormones are **oestrogen** and **progesterone**. These hormones control the menstrual cycle.

- Oestrogen causes the lining of the uterus to thicken and re-grow blood vessels.
- Progesterone maintains the lining of the uterus. A fall in progesterone levels triggers menstruation.

Ovulation is controlled by these hormones together with other hormones produced by the pituitary gland in the brain. We can control **fertility** by using artificial sex hormones (**contraceptive** pill and fertility drugs).

The contraceptive pill lowers fertility. The contraceptive pill mimics female hormones to prevent the body from ovulating. If there are no eggs there can be no fertilisation and no babies. Some drugs, e.g. fertility drugs, promote ovulation and cause more eggs to be released so that there is more chance of fertilisation. Sometimes women donate eggs to infertile women.

Diabetes

Diabetes is caused when the body does not produce enough **insulin**. Insulin converts excess sugar in the blood into glycogen, which is stored in the liver. Diabetes can be controlled by being careful what you eat – avoiding too much sweet food. Some people need to inject themselves with insulin to control their diabetes. The dose of insulin will depend on their diet and how active they are.

Test yourself

1 How are humans adapted to keep warm?

2 Explain the function of oestrogen and progesterone.

3 How does the contraceptive pill prevent pregnancy and how do fertility drugs help a woman to get pregnant?

4 How can a person with diabetes control it?

B1g Gene control & B1h Who am I?

After revising these items you should:

● understand the structure of DNA, chromosomes and genes and how DNA enables us to inherit features from our parents.

DNA, chromosomes and genes

All human body cells except sex cells (**gametes**) have the same number of **chromosomes**. Cells have 46 chromosomes which make up 23 pairs. Different species have different overall numbers of chromosomes.

Chromosomes carry information in the form of **genes**. Chromosomes are long coiled molecules of **DNA** divided into regions called genes. Each gene contains a different sequence of **bases** and this

coded information is called the **genetic code**. The genetic code controls cell activity and some of the characteristics of the organism. All genes are in every cell but only some of them are 'switched on'. Different sets of genes are switched on in different cells, so they all perform their specific function.

Genes are made of a chemical called DNA. Here are some facts about DNA.

● It is the code that makes a human being.

● It can copy itself exactly so the code can be passed on to the next generation.

● It is coiled into a double helix so that it is very small.

● It is so small that it can be stored in the nucleus of every cell.

● It controls how cells function by controlling protein production.

● It is made of chemicals called bases.

● There are four bases whose names are represented by A, T, C and G.

Sexual reproduction

Gametes contain 23 chromosomes, half the number in a body cell.

When gametes join together during fertilisation, the full number of chromosomes is restored to 46. A baby inherits half its DNA from its mother and half from its father, making it a unique individual. Identical twins have exactly the same DNA. Everyone else has different DNA and this leads to variation.

Variation occurs because we inherit different combinations of genes from our parents. Variation is also caused by random fertilisation. Any sperm can fertilise any egg, and both contain different combinations of genes.

How science works

International cooperation has allowed scientists to map every gene in the nucleus of a human cell. This is the Human Genome Project.

This is a massive job which has only been achieved by scientists working together. This is unusual as scientists often work individually or in small groups, and are often competing with each other to make a discovery.

Mutations

DNA can be easily damaged. These changes are called **mutations**. A mutation is a:

- change in the sequence of bases
- removal of one or more bases
- addition of one or more bases.

As a result of a mutation the protein that the gene codes for is changed.

Mutations can be beneficial or harmful. Most are harmful. Mutations can be caused by radiation or chemicals or they can occur spontaneously.

If a mutation occurs in the production of a gamete, the mutation can be passed on to the next generation. These gene mutations are usually recessive and are masked by the correct gene from the other parent. Occasionally a baby gets a faulty gene from both parents, and then the baby will not be healthy. This is why a child may have cystic fibrosis. A child who has one faulty gene should be healthy.

Boy or girl?

Inheritance of sex is controlled by whole chromosomes not individual genes. Humans have two sex chromosomes, X and Y. Males have one X chromosome and one Y chromosome whereas females have two X chromosomes. The punnet square shows how sex is inherited.

<table>
<tr><td></td><td colspan="2" align="center">mum</td></tr>
<tr><td></td><td>X</td><td>X</td></tr>
<tr><td>dad</td><td>X</td><td>XX</td><td>XX</td></tr>
<tr><td></td><td>Y</td><td>XY</td><td>XY</td></tr>
</table>

Alleles

Cells in a baby contain two complete sets of instructions, one from the mother and one from the father. This means there are two versions of every gene, called **alleles**. The baby only uses one of each pair of alleles.

The table shows the meanings of some terms used in genetics.

Term	Meaning
dominant allele	these alleles are the code that is used
recessive allele	these alleles are the code that is not used
homozygous	two alleles are the same
heterozygous	two alleles are different

The dominant allele is always represented by a capital letter. The recessive allele is represented by the same letter in lower case.

Breeding experiments

Mendel carried out experiments using pea plants. He crossed a homozygous tall plant with a homozygous short plant and found that all the offspring were tall. This type of cross using one characteristic is a monohybrid cross. It can be shown in two ways.

<table>
<tr><td></td><td colspan="2" align="center">tall</td></tr>
<tr><td></td><td>T</td><td>T</td></tr>
<tr><td>short</td><td>t</td><td>Tt</td><td>Tt</td></tr>
<tr><td></td><td>t</td><td>Tt</td><td>Tt</td></tr>
</table>

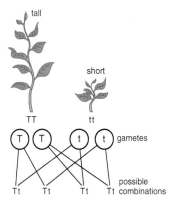

It is possible for two tall pea plants to produce short plants. The punnet square below shows the genetic diagram.

<table>
<tr><td></td><td colspan="2" align="center">tall</td></tr>
<tr><td></td><td>T</td><td>t</td></tr>
<tr><td>tall</td><td>T</td><td>TT</td><td>Tt</td></tr>
<tr><td></td><td>t</td><td>Tt</td><td>tt</td></tr>
</table>

Genes or environment?

Scientists are trying to determine the relative importance of our genes versus the environment in making us who we are. It is a combination of both, but we don't know how much each one contributes.

There is a big debate about this in relation to intelligence, sporting ability and health.

Do you really want to know?

The table shows the benefits and disadvantages of knowing whether we have a genetic disorder that can be passed on to our children.

Benefits	Disadvantages
Knowing about our genes can enable us to decide whether or not to have children. If we knew that both our partner and ourselves were carriers for the cystic fibrosis gene, we would know that there was a one in four risk of having a child with cystic fibrosis. We would then decide whether or not to have children or take some other course of action, such as having the gametes checked, to see if they were normal.	Society has not yet decided who owns the right to know about our personal DNA.
If we knew we had a high risk of dying from heart disease we could be more careful about our lifestyle and the food that we ate.	Some insurance companies are asking clients if they have ever had any DNA tests. If they find that the person is at risk they may refuse to insure that person or raise their premiums. This will enable them to make more money for their shareholders and keep premiums down for their other clients. This means that some people may be put off having tests to find out if they are at risk from genetic disease.

Exam tip

You must be able to state both sides of an argument in questions about opinions.

Test yourself

1 Name the gametes in a human.

2 Explain how gender is inherited.

3 What does heterozygous mean?

4 In Mendel's experiments with pea plants, he crossed two tall plants together and obtained plants with these genotypes.

   Complete the table to show which plants will be tall and which will be short. What is the ratio of tall to short plants?

Genotype	Tall or short?
TT	
Tt	
tT	
tt	

5 Huntington's disease is a genetic disorder that affects one in 20 000 people.

   Huntington's disease is caused by a dominant faulty allele (H).

   The diagram shows a family tree.

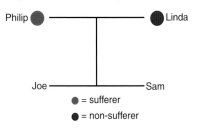

   ● = sufferer
   ● = non-sufferer

   (a) What are the genotypes of Philip and Linda?
   (b) What is the probability of both Joe and Sam inheriting the condition?

B2a Ecology in our school grounds & B2b Grouping organisms

After revising these items you should:

- be able to group organisms, understand the inter-relationships between organisms and their habitats and explain sampling methods.

Counting and identifying organisms

It is difficult to count all the organisms in an **ecosystem**. Instead scientists sample the **populations** of organisms in order to get an estimate of the total number of individuals. A population is a breeding group of animals or plants in the ecosystem and there are many ways of sampling it, for example:

- **quadrats** • pooters • pit-fall traps
- nets • capture and release.

Limitations of counting and collecting methods:

- Sample size will affect accuracy of estimate.
- Samples may be unrepresentative of the population.

Exam tip

You should know how to use each of the sampling methods and remember that the sample must be large enough to be representative.

When studying an ecosystem, it is important to be able to identify the organisms that live in it. This can be done by using a **key**. Keys divide organisms into smaller and smaller groups.

Ecosystems

An ecosystem is a place or **habitat** together with all the organisms that live there. Examples of natural ecosystems are:

- rainforest • river • meadow • desert

These ecosystems have many different **species** living in them. They have a high **biodiversity**.

Other ecosystems are created by humans. These are artificial and usually have a lower biodiversity.

One example is a field of wheat. The farmer has to use pesticides to stop other species growing and fertilisers to make the wheat grow well.

Some ecosystems are still unexplored and may contain undiscovered species.

Classification

All livings organisms are different and can be put into groups. This is called classification. Organisms can be classified into animals and plants.

Characteristics that place an organism into the animal kingdom
They can move independently.
They do not have chloroplasts.
They cannot make their own food.
They are more compact (this helps with movement).

Characteristics that place an organism into the plant kingdom
They cannot move independently.
They contain chloroplasts, which makes them green.
They can make their own food.
They spread out more (because they cannot move).

Some organisms cannot be placed into one of these two groups, because they have characteristics which place them in both or neither group; for example Fungi and *Euglena*.

Animals can be divided into two groups:

- **Vertebrates** – animals with backbones.
- **Invertebrates** – animals without backbones.

The table shows the five vertebrate groups, an example of each and the characteristics of the group.

Group	Example	Characteristics
fish	salmon	wet scales gills
amphibian	frog	moist permeable skin
reptile	crocodile	dry scales
bird	blackbird	feathers beak
mammal	human	fur produces milk

Archaeopteryx is an example of an organism that is difficult to classify. It does not fit into one of the vertebrate groups because it has both reptilian and bird features.

Species

Organisms are further divided until there is only one type of organism in the group. This group is a species. Every species has two names. This way of naming species is called the **binomial** system.

How science works

Scientists realised that there were many different types of organisms in the world. They collected information about these organisms and tried to put them into groups. This helped to develop the way organisms are classified.

Now when a new organism is found, it is placed into a kingdom and eventually needs a binomial name.

The first name is the same as similar animals but the second name is often based on the person who discovered it.

Organisms that belong to the same species are capable of interbreeding to produce fertile offspring.

Occasionally members of different species can reproduce. Their offspring are **hybrids**. Animal hybrids are infertile and cannot reproduce. It is difficult to classify hybrids.

Species that are similar tend to live in similar types of habitats. If they live in different habitats then they may have different features because they need different features to survive. Although their features are different, they may have evolved from a common ancestor. The diagram shows the ancestry of humans and apes.

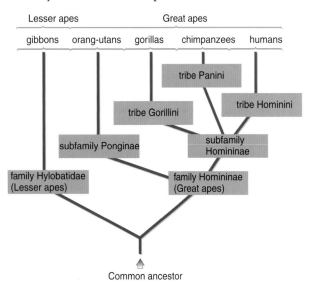

Common ancestor

Exam tip

You do not need to learn this diagram for the exam but you could be given the information and asked to use it.

Different species that live in the same habitat have evolved similar features so that they can survive in that habitat. Dolphins and whales are mammals but appear similar to sharks, which are fish. This is because these organisms all have to be able to swim in water, so they are streamlined and have fins.

Similarities and differences between species can be explained by **evolution** and ecological relationships.

Test yourself

1 Give two examples of unexplored ecosystems.

2 In a 0.5 square metre quadrat 20 dandelion plants are counted. Estimate how many dandelions there are in a 100 square metre field. Why might this answer be inaccurate? Explain how you could get a better estimate of the number of dandelion plants in this field.

3 The diagram shows five organisms.

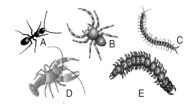

Use this key to identify them.

		Yes	No
1	Does it have more than 10 legs?	go to 2	go to 3
2	Does it have two pairs of legs per segment?	millipede	centipede
3	Does it have three parts to its body?	insect	go to 4
4	Does it have eight legs?	arachnid	crustacean

4 Name a group of organisms which have neither animal nor plant characteristics.

5 Name an organism which has both animal and plant characteristics.

6 What is the binomial name of a human?

7 Mules are hybrids. How are they produced?

B2c The food factory

After revising this item you should:

- understand how plants make food by photosynthesis, how the rate of photosynthesis can be increased and how plants use the food they make.

Photosynthesis

Plants make their own food by a process called photosynthesis.

$$\text{carbon dioxide} + \text{water} \xrightarrow[\text{chlorophyll}]{\text{light energy}} \text{glucose} + \text{oxygen}$$

$$6CO_2 + 6H_2O \xrightarrow[\text{chlorophyll}]{\text{light energy}} C_6H_{12}O_6 + 6O_2$$

Exam tip

You should know the word and symbol equations for photosynthesis.

Try to remember that the gases carbon dioxide and oxygen are involved and they come in alphabetical order. Also water and glucose are in the equation, not in alphabetical order.

Plants make food and either use it to carry out their daily processes or store it for future use. Animals eat plants and so the energy the plants have trapped is passed on in the food chain to the animals. Plants are essential to all life on our planet. They also return oxygen to the atmosphere to be used in respiration.

The glucose made during photosynthesis is transported as soluble sugars to all parts of the plant, where it can be used or stored as insoluble **starch**. Glucose and starch can be converted into other substances that the plant needs. Glucose is:

- used for respiration
- converted to **cellulose** for cell walls
- converted to protein for growth and repair
- converted to starch, **oils** and fats for storage.

The insoluble substances cannot leave the cell: this is why they are used for storage.

In the summer plants grow faster because there is more light and more warmth. This is because they can carry out more photosynthesis. Farmers want photosynthesis to go faster so they can grow more food. Farmers can increase photosynthesis by giving plants more:

- light
- carbon dioxide
- warmth

How science works

Scientists use technology in glasshouses to adjust the level of these three factors so that they can be carefully controlled to give optimum conditions for maximum growth.

They use heaters to increase the temperature and these give out carbon dioxide so the level of carbon dioxide increases as well.

When it is warm and there is no need for heaters, there is no increase in carbon dioxide.

Limiting factors

If light, carbon dioxide or warmth is in short supply, it becomes a **limiting factor**. This is because a shortage of one of these factors will limit the rate of photosynthesis.

The three graphs show what happens when each factor increases, while the others are kept constant.

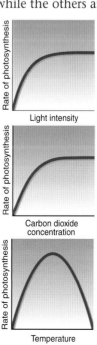

In the first two graphs, initially the rate increases – it then becomes constant even though that factor is still increasing. This is because another factor is in short supply and is limiting the rate. In the third graph the temperature is increasing. This eventually denatures the plant's enzymes and so the rate drops to zero.

Respiration versus photosynthesis

All living organisms including plants respire all of the time. If they do not they die. When they respire they take in oxygen and give out carbon dioxide. Plants also take in carbon dioxide and give out oxygen as they photosynthesise during the day.

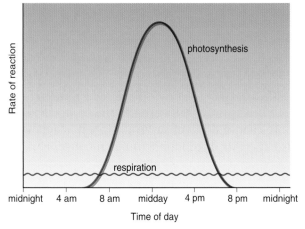

Plants photosynthesise faster than they respire – so during the day they give out more oxygen than they use and absorb more carbon dioxide than they release.

Test yourself

1 Where do the raw materials for photosynthesis come from and what is the energy source?

2 How can a glasshouse in your garden be provided with more light, warmth and carbon dioxide?

3 Look at the graph of respiration and photosynthesis. How does the shape of this graph change at different times of the day? How would the shape be different if the rate was measured in winter?

4 Look at the graph of light intensity against rate of photosynthesis (page 17). Explain what is happening when the curve is going up and when the curve plateaus.

5 Look at the graph of temperature against rate of photosynthesis (page 17). Explain what is happening when the curve is falling.

B2d Compete or die & B2e Adapt to fit

After revising these items you should:

● understand how animals and plants compete with or rely on each other and that changing our environment affects animal and plant distributions.

Competition

Every organism is in **competition** with every other organism. Organisms compete for:

• food • water • shelter
• light • minerals

This competition may affect the distribution and population size of animals and plants.

Competition ensures that the population of any one species does not get too big. When a population does get too big, something usually happens to bring it down again.

Exam tip

You should know how species of organisms compete to survive and breed.

Competition between species

There is also competition between different species. This happens because a habitat can only support so many species. They are competing for the same space and food. The most successful species survive and the least successful ones die. The organisms are competing for the same **ecological niche**, for example:

• red and grey squirrel
• ladybird and harlequin ladybird
• mink and otter.

Predator and prey

Predators and prey both affect the size of each other's population. The graph shows the relationship between the populations of lions (predator) and zebra (prey).

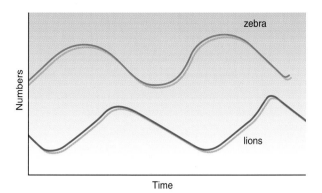

This cyclic relationship helps to maintain the balance in numbers of each species and stops any population increase getting out of control.

Parasitism and mutualism

A parasite is an organism that lives on or in another living organism. The organism they live on is the host. The parasite benefits and the host loses.

Parasites of humans include:

• tapeworm • flea

The tapeworm:

• grows in the gut of animals
• feeds off the food the animal eats
• can cause blockage in the host's gut
• can grow up to several metres long.

Fleas suck blood from their host. This can weaken the host and introduce dangerous diseases.

Some organisms live together. Where both organisms benefit from the relationship it is called **mutualism**. The oxpecker bird eats the small parasites that live in the fur of mammals (buffalo). This ensures that the oxpecker survives and is successful and the buffalo gets rid of its parasites.

The close interdependence ensures that when one organism survives and is successful, the other one is too. It determines the distribution and abundance of different organisms in different habitats.

The mutualistic relationship between nitrogen fixing bacteria which live in root nodules of leguminous plants means that the plant has more nitrates and so can make more protein and the bacteria is provided with sugars for food. The bacteria convert atmospheric nitrogen into nitrates which the plants can use to make protein.

Adaptations

Animals are **adapted** to live in their environment. They will have adapted to that environment over a long period of time. This is so they can survive and compete for limited resources.

The more quickly an organism can adapt the more chance it has of survival. How it adapts will also affect its distribution and abundance. For example:

• organisms that have adapted to dry conditions will live in a desert
• those that have adapted to live in water are found in lakes, rivers and the sea.

How is a camel adapted to life in the desert?

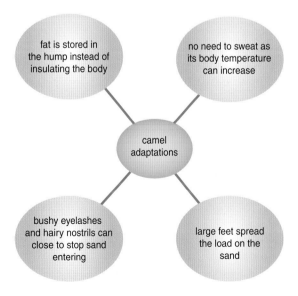

The table shows how a polar bear is adapted to life in the Arctic.

Feature	How it adapts the polar bear
thick fur	for insulation
white fur	for camouflage
layer of fat	for insulation
sharp claws and teeth	to catch and eat prey
strong legs	for running and swimming
large feet	to spread the load on snow
fur on soles of feet	for insulation and grip
small ears	small surface area when compared to body

Plants are also adapted to their environments. The cactus is adapted to hot, dry conditions in these ways:

- Rounded shape gives reduced surface area/volume ratio to reduce water loss and store water.
- Thick cuticle reduces water loss.
- Leaves reduced to spines reduce water loss and discourage animals.
- Green stem allows photosynthesis.
- Water storage to withstand droughts.
- Long roots reach down to water.

Adaptation for pollination

Pollination is the transfer of pollen from the anther of the stamen to the stigma.

In order to reproduce, plants must be pollinated. So that pollination is successful, plants are adapted to pollination by wind or by insects.

Wind-pollinated plants:	Insect-pollinated plants:
• feathery stigmas • small, light pollen	• colourful petals • sticky pollen • nectar

Test yourself

1 Name three things that can happen to stop a population increasing.

2 Why is the small surface area of a polar bear's ears compared to its body size important?

3 Look at the diagrams of two flowers.

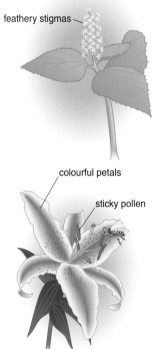

feathery stigmas

colourful petals

sticky pollen

  (a) The yellow flower is pollinated by the wind. Suggest three features of the diagram which show this.

  (b) How is the pink flower pollinated?

  (c) Give three features which support your decision in (b).

4 Explain how mutualism works.

B2f Survival of the fittest

The fossil record

The **fossil** record refers to all the fossils found in different layers of rock. The different layers of rock help scientists to work out the age of the fossil and know which are the oldest and which are the youngest.

Scientists believe that the clues to our origins lie in the fossil record. Animals and plants can change over long periods of time and fossils provide evidence for this. Fossils can give us evidence of organisms that lived long ago.

The fossil record has been interpreted differently over time:

- Creationists, who believe that their God created all life on Earth, believe that God created the fossil record too.

- Most scientists think that the fossil record provides evidence for evolution of life on Earth over millions of years. This makes the Earth much older than when creationists believe God created it (a few thousand years ago).

The fossil record is not complete because:

- some fossils have not yet been discovered
- some organisms do not produce fossils – soft tissue usually decays and does not fossilise
- fossilisation rarely occurs.

How fossils are formed

Fossils form over time in different ways. The boxes show three of these.

A	The hard body parts (shells, bones, leaves) of a dead organism are covered with sediment. These body parts are gradually replaced by minerals which form the fossil.
B	Casts and impressions of the body are made in rock.
C	The body is preserved whole in: • amber • peat bogs • tar pits • ice

The fossil record of a horse's leg has provided information of the evolution of the horse.

The palaeontologist Marsh described three fossil horses he found, Orohippus, Miohippus and Hipparion. As more fossil horses were discovered, it became clear that the evolution of the horse was complicated. The horse evolved to run fast. Early horses ran on four fingers, modern horses run on the middle finger only.

The diagrams show the changes over time of a horse's teeth, legs and body shape.

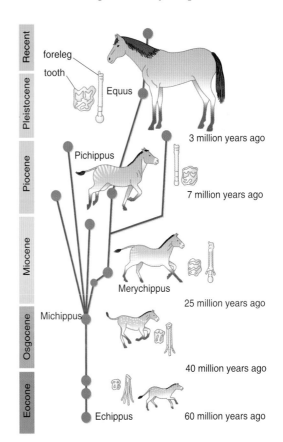

Natural selection

When environments change some animal and plant species survive or evolve but many become **extinct** because they cannot change quickly enough.

Those organisms that are better adapted to their environment are more likely to survive. This is called **natural selection**.

Darwin put forward this theory. It contains several stages.

- Members of the same species are different from each other. This is natural variation.
- Each organism is in competition with every other for limited resources.
- Some are better adapted than others and so survive and reproduce (survival of the fittest).
- The offspring inherit these successful adaptations.
- Those without the successful characteristics die.
- Those unable to compete become extinct.

Over time the changes brought about by natural selection may result in the formation of a new species.

Adaptations are controlled by genes. Genes are passed on to the next generation.

Natural selection is still going on today. Examples include:

- The peppered moth was grey and well camouflaged on the light bark of trees. During the industrial revolution the bark was covered in soot and the moths were no longer hidden. Some moths were slightly darker and more camouflaged so they survived and reproduced. Within a few years all the moths were darker.

Exam tip

*You should be able to explain the occurrence of dark and pale forms of the peppered moth in areas with different levels of **pollution**. There are more dark moths in areas where pollution is higher and more light coloured moths in areas of less pollution.*

- Bacteria are becoming resistant to antibiotics. This is because when antibiotics are used to treat disease, some bacteria survive and breed. Their resistance is passed on to the next generation. Soon they are all resistant.
- Rats are becoming resistant to the rat poison warfarin. Rats are fussy about their food. They eat a little bit. If they like it they will return to eat more. The warfarin will kill some before they return. Those rats that are not killed are resistant to warfarin and survive to breed. Soon all rats are resistant to warfarin and another poison has to be found.

How science works

When we have a bacterial infection, the doctor prescribes antibiotics to kill the bacteria and we get better. But some bacteria may mutate and become resistant.

The doctor can try a different antibiotic but again some bacteria may mutate and become resistant. This leads to multi-resistant strains of bacteria, which are difficult to control and are becoming a big problem in hospitals.

Scientists are currently trying to solve this problem.

Sometimes a population gets separated into two breeding groups. These two populations evolve independently and may not be able to breed with each other. This means they are now two different species.

There are other theories of evolution besides Darwin's. Lamarck's theory of inheritance of acquired characteristics is one of them, but it was discredited because acquired characteristics do not have a genetic basis.

It is important to see all the evidence before coming to a conclusion about a theory. Many new theories have been met with hostility before all the evidence was considered.

1 Fossils give us clues to the origins of life. Explain why the fossil record is incomplete.

2 Look at the diagrams of a horse's leg.

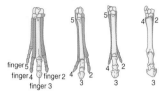

finger 5
finger 4 finger 2
finger 3

Orohippus   Miohippus   Hipparion   Equus (modern horse)

Describe how the horse's leg has changed over time.

3 (a) Describe the stages in Darwin's theory of evolution.

 (b) Explain how Lamarck's theory is different.

4 The sentences describe how antibiotic resistance develops.
They are in the wrong order. Put them in the correct order.

 A some resistant bacteria survive
 B some bacteria are killed
 C soon they are all resistant
 D antibiotics are given to a person to kill bacteria
 E their resistance is passed on to the next generation
 F the surviving resistant bacteria breed

5 Explain how rats have become resistant to warfarin.

B2g Population out of control?

● be able to explain what effect the increasing human population is having on the environment and understand the use of living and non-living indicators of pollution.

The problem

The human population is increasing. More people means we are using more of the world's **resources** and producing more pollution. If the rate of increase continues the Earth will not be able to sustain all the people living on it. Some countries are already taking steps to slow down the rate of increase. The graph shows how the human population has grown over the last 2000 years.

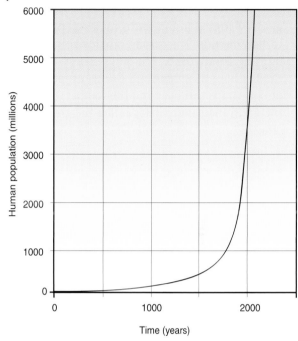

In parts of the world the human population is growing **exponentially**. This means that the population doubles every 53 years. The possible consequences are:

● running out of food

● not enough space

● build up of waste with no space to dispose of it.

Each of these will have a negative impact on the population as a whole.

Pollution

The table shows the population and the amount of carbon dioxide produced by Africa and the USA.

Place	Population (millions)	Carbon dioxide produced (billions of tonnes)
Africa	732	0.4
USA	265	4.9

The developed countries of the world such as the USA have a small proportion of the world's population compared to less developed countries such as those in Africa. But they produce more of the pollutant carbon dioxide and use more of the resources.

As pollution increases the consequences for the world also increase. Effects include:

- global warming from increasing levels of carbon dioxide. The carbon dioxide comes from burning **fossil fuels**. The Sun's energy enters the Earth's atmosphere and warms it up. Carbon dioxide traps this heat and the temperature of the Earth increases. This is called the greenhouse effect.

- **ozone** depletion from CFCs in the upper atmosphere. Ozone is in the upper atmosphere and absorbs the ultraviolet (UV) rays from the Sun. UV rays are harmful to humans. Pollutants like CFCs damage the ozone layer and let in the harmful UV rays.

- **acid rain** from sulfur dioxide. This gas is produced when fossil fuels are burned. It dissolves in rain in the atmosphere and produces an acid. This acid falls as rain. It acidifies lakes and kills fish and trees. Acid rain also dissolves **limestone** and this affects many of our buildings and statues.

How science works

Technological developments have often had damaging effects on our environment. Burning fossil fuels has resulted in acid rain to such an extent that large areas of forest have been destroyed when this falls.

Also the acid water gets into lakes and rivers and kills all of the living organisms. These living organisms could be the food supply of another animal or human population.

Measuring pollution

Pollution can be measured by using living indicators – we call these **indicator species**.

The table shows some indicator species and where they live.

Indicator species	Where they live
bloodworm waterlouse	polluted water (little oxygen)
rat-tailed maggot sludgeworm	very polluted water
lichen	clean air (little air pollution)

Exam tip

You may be given some data, e.g. a map showing the distribution of an indicator species. You should be able to analyse it and draw conclusions.

Test yourself

1. Name three of the Earth's resources that are being used up.

2. What are the possible consequences of the human population increasing exponentially?

3. Explain how burning fossil fuels causes global warming.

4. How does sulfur dioxide in the air contribute to acid rain?

5. Look at the table below. It shows how much sulfur dioxide different lichen species can tolerate.

Lichen	Level of sulfur dioxide tolerated ($\mu g/m^3$)
no lichens	175
Lechanora sp.	125
Parmelia sp.	50
Usnea sp.	0

(a) What level of sulfur dioxide stops lichens growing?

(b) Suggest which lichen(s) will grow where sulfur dioxide levels are 50 $\mu g/m^3$?

B2h Sustainability

After revising this item you should:

- understand why organisms become extinct, explain how endangered species can be protected, explain sustainable development and understand what choices we have to achieve this.

Endangered and extinct

When all the individuals in a species die, the species becomes extinct. Extinction can happen naturally as a result of **climate change** or by competition with another species.

A species that is likely to become extinct is an **endangered** species.

There are several reasons why an organism may become extinct:

- When humans develop areas of the countryside, they destroy the habitats of some organisms. If that is the only place in the world where those organisms live they will become extinct.
- Humans hunt animals to eat or for their skin. This can reduce the numbers so much that they become an endangered species.
- Humans pollute the environment of living organisms so that they can no longer live there. They must move or die.

We are responsible for many of these problems so what can we do to help the situation?

protecting habitats	Protect habitats that contain rare or endangered species. Sites of Special Scientific Interest can be set up to prevent the land being developed.
education	Teach people about the organisms and their habitat and how important it is to look after it.
legal protection	Laws make it illegal to harm certain species.
captive breeding programmes	Breed rare and endangered species in captivity and then release them back into the environment.
artificial ecosystems	Create new ecosystems for endangered species to live in.

Conservation

The more we look after our environment, the more species will survive. The more species there are in any one habitat, the more likely it is to survive, and small changes in the habitat can usually be accommodated. There are many reasons for conserving our environment:

- To protect the human food supply. If we damage our environment we put our food supply at risk.
- To discover new plants that could provide us with medicines in the future.
- To minimise damage to food chains and webs, so other organisms can find food.
- To look after endangered species.
- To preserve our cultural heritage for future generations.

Sustainable development

When we remove something from our environment, we should replace it to protect that environment. This is called **sustainable development**.

As the world population grows, more and more resources are being used up. The demand for food and energy is constantly growing. We are producing more waste products and we have less land to dispose of them.

In order to maintain this growing population, feed them and dispose of their waste, we must encompass sustainable development.

Educating the public plays an important part in sustaining our environment and protecting endangered species for future generations.

The table shows how we can replace some of those things we remove – and so sustain our resources.

Removed item	How to replace
cut down trees	replant with young trees so that when they grow they can be cut down
fish	introduce quotas so that fish stocks do not get too low
	limit the minimum size of fish that can be caught so that the young ones have a chance to grow and reproduce

Sustainable development may protect endangered species by replacing those individuals that have been killed. For example, where forests are cut down to provide wood, we should plant new trees so that there will be trees for future generations to use.

Exam tip

You should be able to explain the idea of sustainable development and apply it to specific situations.

Whales

These mammals have commercial value both during their lives and when dead.

- Alive – attract tourists and bring in money.
- Dead – bodies are used for food, oil and cosmetics.

Scientists still have a lot to learn about whales. For example:

- how they survive at extreme depths
- how they communicate over long distances
- their migration patterns from one part of the world to another to find food or a mate.

How science works

International cooperation is needed to protect the whales from those who hunt them. But whales live far out in the oceans – and it is difficult to enforce laws on whaling because they are usually found in international waters.

Some countries, e.g. Japan, continue whaling, claiming they do it for scientific research reasons.

Some whales are bred and live in captivity. Their behaviour is studied by scientists who try to understand more about them. They are also used as entertainment in aquariums.

Exam tip

Where an ethical issue is involved you should be able to:

- *state clearly what the issue is*
- *summarise different views that may be held.*

Test yourself

1 Trees are being felled in tropical rainforests. Scientists have noticed that there are fewer types of animals and plants in these deforested regions. Explain why.

2 List the ways in which humans can help endangered species.

3 Why is the panda an endangered species?

4 Explain how cutting down trees and replanting more trees is an example of sustainable development.

5 Whales are kept in captivity for human research and entertainment. Give one reason for and one reason against each of these uses.

C1a Cooking & C1b Food additives

After revising these items you should:

● know about food cooking, additives and packaging.

Why do we cook food?

Some foods are eaten raw but most are cooked.

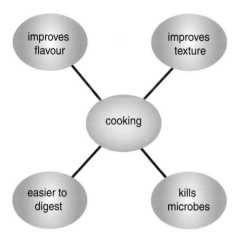

How science works

Some eggs have been found to contain bacteria called Salmonella, which can cause food poisoning.

Many people still choose to eat eggs with runny yolks. A runny yolk has not been cooked enough to kill Salmonella.

Suggest why people take this risk.

Chemical change

Cooking food is a chemical change because:

• a new substance is formed

• the change cannot be reversed (it is irreversible).

Eggs and meat are good sources of proteins. Protein molecules change shape when eggs and meat are cooked and cannot be changed back. This process is called denaturing. This is why egg white changes from a transparent liquid to a white solid as it is cooked.

Potatoes are a good source of **carbohydrates**. As a potato is cooked, cellulose cell walls break down releasing the cell contents. This makes the potato softer and easier to chew. It also makes it easier to digest.

Baking powder

Baking powder is added to cake mixture. The baking powder contains sodium hydrogencarbonate. When heated this breaks down, giving off the gas carbon dioxide.

$$2NaHCO_3 \rightarrow Na_2CO_3 + H_2O + CO_2$$

sodium hydrogen carbonate $\rightarrow$ sodium carbonate + water + carbon dioxide

The carbon dioxide gas expands in the cake mixture, making the cake rise as it is cooked.

We can show that carbon dioxide is given off in this reaction by bubbling the gas through limewater. Carbon dioxide turns limewater cloudy.

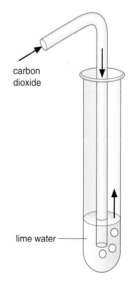

carbon dioxide

lime water

Food additives

Food additives are chemicals added to the food during processing. All approved additives are given **E-numbers**. The E-number of an additive tells us why it has been added to the food.

E-number	Type of additive	Why it is added	Some foods it is added to
E100–199	food colours	improve appearance	sweets, soft drinks, jellies
E200–299	preservatives	stop food going bad	jams, squashes
E300–399	**antioxidants**	stop reaction with oxygen	meat pies, salad cream
E400–499	**emulsifiers**	keep foods mixed	margarine, mayonnaise, salad cream
E600–699	flavourings and flavour enhancers	improve taste	sweets, meat products

Exam tip

You do not need to learn E-numbers, but in an exam you may be given information similar to that in the table and asked questions about it.

Exam tip

In exam marks are sometimes given for using the correct scientific terms, such as hydrophobic and hydrophilic.

How science works

Several children at a playgroup became hyperactive. All of the children at the playgroup had drunk the same brand of orange squash, which contains several food colouring additives.

These facts suggest a correlation between hyperactivity and these additives.

What additional information is needed to support the idea that these additives cause hyperactivity?

Emulsifiers

If you shake up oil and water they seem to mix. If you leave this for a few minutes the oil and water separate out again. Emulsifiers are added to food to keep the oil (or fat) and water mixed as an **emulsion**.

Emulsifiers are molecules that have a **hydrophilic** (water loving) part and a **hydrophobic** (water hating but oil or fat loving) part. The hydrophilic head of the molecule bonds to water molecules. The hydrophobic tail bonds with oil molecules. This keeps the oil and water mixed.

Emulsifiers turn water and oil into emulsions

Packaging

The way that food is packaged can help to make it stay fresh for longer. Intelligent packaging can be used to improve the quality and safety of food. The material used for active packaging controls or reacts with what is taking place inside the packaging.

- If fruit is wrapped in film that has tiny holes, oxygen can enter and keep the fruit fresh for longer.
- Biscuits are wrapped in film without holes to keep out oxygen and water, so the biscuits stay crisp.
- Some foods have all of the water removed from inside the packing so that moulds cannot grow and make the food rot.
- It is possible to make cans that will heat or cool the drink inside. You can have a hot cup of coffee or an ice cold cola anywhere.

How science works

Many modern food packagings are made from plastics made from crude oil. In the past many food products were put into paper bags.

Explain one advantage for food packaging of using plastics instead of paper, and one advantage of using paper instead of plastics.

1 Why does potato taste different when it has been cooked?

2 How does the appearance of a cake show that sodium hydrogencarbonate in baking powder added to the cake mixture has decomposed as the cake cooked?

3 If meat pies are made without adding antioxidants, what may happen when they are stored for a few days?

4 Mayonnaise contains vegetable oil and vinegar. Why must it also contain an emulsifier?

5 Why do fruit and biscuits need different sorts of packaging?

C1c Smells

After revising this item you should:

● know about the use of esters in perfumes.

Making an ester

Esters are organic compounds with characteristic sweet smells. Mixtures of different esters are used to create the distinctive smells of perfumes. An ester is made by the reaction of an alcohol with an acid.

alcohol + organic acid ⟶ ester + water

You could make an ester, with supervision from your teacher, by following these instructions.

1 Put a few cubic centimetres (cm^3) of an alcohol, such as ethanol, in a test tube.

2 Add a similar volume of an organic acid, such as ethanoic acid, and stir.

3 Add one drop of concentrated sulfuric acid to act as a **catalyst** and speed up the reaction.

4 Place the test tube in a beaker of hot water for a few minutes to safely heat the mixture.

5 Pour the mixture into a beaker half filled with cold water.

Droplets of ester can be seen on the surface.

This equation shows the reaction that takes place between ethanol and ethanoic acid.

ethanol + ethanoic acid ⟶ ethyl ethanoate + water

When we show this reaction using displayed formulae it is possible to see how the two molecules join together with the loss of a water molecule.

The ester ethyl ethanoate can be recognised by its sweet smell.

Esters are responsible for the sweet smell of flowers and fruit. Many of these naturally occurring esters can be manufactured in a laboratory.

Different **solvents** can be used for different jobs, because they will dissolve different **solutes**. The table below shows which solvents will dissolve wax and salt.

Solvent	Wax	Salt
ethyl ethanoate	dissolves	does not dissolve
hexane	dissolves	does not dissolve
water	does not dissolve	dissolves

Perfume properties

Each perfume has its own recognisable smell because the esters stimulate cells in the nose. To work successfully a perfume must have a number of properties.

Property of perfume	Why it is needed
evaporates easily (volatile)	so that the smelly esters can easily reach the nose
non-toxic	so that it does not poison you
does not react with water	so that it does not react with perspiration (sweat)
does not irritate the skin	so that it can be put onto the skin without causing harm
insoluble in water	so that it does not wash off easily

Volatility

The ease with which a liquid can evaporate is called its volatility. The esters in a perfume have a fairly high volatility, so that they can quickly evaporate into the air and reach the nose.

The volatility of perfumes can be explained by kinetic theory.

- During evaporation particles escape from the liquid into the air.
- Only particles with lots of energy can escape the attraction of other particles in the liquid to evaporate.
- In a perfume the attraction between the particles is weak, so the particles do not need much energy to evaporate.

This is why the esters in perfumes are volatile.

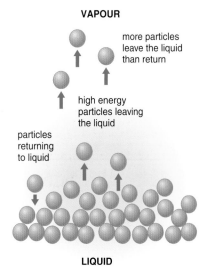

Solvents

If you have painted your nails and get fed up with the colour you will want to remove the nail varnish. It will not wash off with water, but you can remove it using nail varnish remover.

- The nail varnish is insoluble in water, but is soluble in the nail varnish remover.
- The nail varnish is a solute because it dissolves in the solvent in the nail varnish remover.
- This forms a **solution** which does not separate out.

To explain why water will not dissolve nail varnish we need to think about the attraction between particles.

- The attraction between water molecules is stronger than the attraction between water molecules and the particles in the nail varnish.
- The attraction between particles in the nail varnish is also stronger than that between water molecules and the particles in the nail varnish.
- So the attraction between water molecules and the particles in the nail varnish is not strong enough to pull the particles in the nail varnish into the water to make a solution.

Esters can be used as solvents. Ethyl ethanoate is the solvent in nail varnish remover. It has a strong enough attraction with the particles in the nail varnish to form a solution.

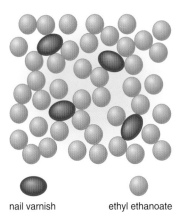

nail varnish   ethyl ethanoate

Testing cosmetics

Before a company can sell a cosmetic product to the public, the product must be tested. This is to make sure that it is safe for people to use.

The cosmetic must not be poisonous and must not cause irritation to the skin. Only when the company is certain that there are no problems is the cosmetic product marketed.

Cosmetics may be tested on animals first. The testing of cosmetics on animals is banned in the United Kingdom, but is allowed in some other countries.

Advantages of testing cosmetics on animals:

- quick   •   cheap

Disadvantages of testing cosmetics on animals:

- Results on animals may not be the same as on humans.
- Many people object to animals being used for these tests.

How science works

Look at these two statements about the results of some animal experiments carried out to test a new cosmetic.

Animal rights protester: 'The results from these tests are meaningless. They are making animals suffer for no useful reason.'

Scientist working for a cosmetics company: 'The results from these experiments will help us to decide whether this product is safe for people to use.'

Suggest why these two people have made different conclusions from the same results.

Test yourself

1 When making esters, the mixture of different chemicals is heated in a water bath rather than using a Bunsen burner. Suggest Why.

2 Why may a company prefer to make an ester synthetically rather than extract it from a plant?

3 The esters in a perfume are dissolved in an organic solvent. This is much more volatile than the esters. Suggest why this is important.

4 Salt dissolves in water but not in ethyl ethanoate. Suggest why.

5 Some people who are against testing cosmetics on animals are not against testing medicinal drugs on animals. Suggest why.

C1d Making crude oil useful

After revising this item you should:

- know how useful products are obtained from crude oil.

Fossil fuels

Fossil fuels:

- include **crude oil**, coal and gas
- are **finite resources** of energy because one day they will run out
- are **non-renewable**.

Crude oil supplies

Large tanker ships or long pipelines are used to take the crude oil from the wells to a refinery, where it is made into useful products. Accidents can cause crude oil to be spilled, polluting land or sea and killing wildlife.

Many of the largest reserves of oil are concentrated in a few countries where there is political unrest. These countries control the output and price of the world's most important energy resource.

Developed countries such as the UK and USA are dependent on imported oil as their main source of energy. Supply restrictions and price rises can cause damage to the economies of these countries.

How science works

Transporting crude oil in tanker ships can lead to serious damage to the environment if there is an accident. Despite this possibility, millions of tons of crude oil are transported across the seas each year.

Suggest why oil is transported in this way.

Fractional distillation

Crude oil contains **hydrocarbon** molecules of different sizes, ranging from those with just one carbon atom to those with over 50 carbon atoms. The displayed formulae of four of these hydrocarbon molecules are shown below.

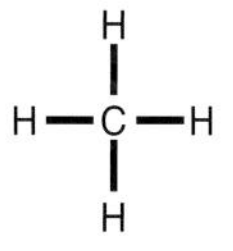

methane (CH_4)

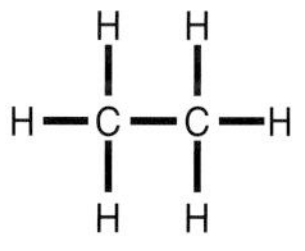

ethane (C_2H_6)

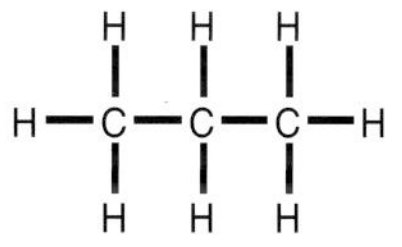

propane (C_3H_8)

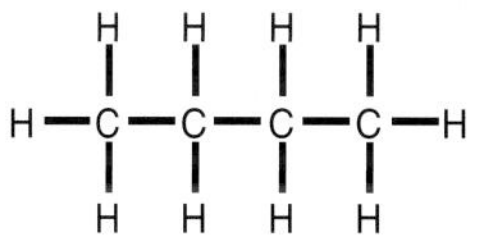

butane (C_4H_{10})

To make useful products from crude oil it is separated into **fractions** using a **fractional distillation** column.

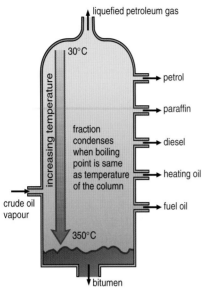

In hydrocarbon molecules the hydrogen and carbon atoms are held together by very strong **covalent** bonds. These do not break when the hydrocarbon boils.

The **intermolecular** forces between hydrocarbon molecules are much weaker. When the hydrocarbon boils these break, releasing the molecules as a vapour.

The intermolecular forces between large hydrocarbon molecules are stronger than those between small hydrocarbon molecules. So the larger the hydrocarbon molecules the more energy is needed to separate them, and therefore the higher the **boiling point**.

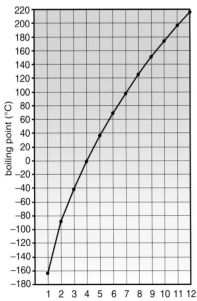

Fractional distillation works like this:

- The fractionating column is hottest at the bottom and coldest at the top.
- As crude oil vapour passes up the column it cools and each hydrocarbon condenses when it reaches its boiling point.
- This means that hydrocarbon molecules of different sizes condense at different heights up the column.
- Each fraction, containing several hydrocarbons with similar boiling points, is collected to make a different product.
- The nearer the top of the column the fraction is collected, the lower the boiling points and the smaller the molecules of the hydrocarbons it contains.

Supply and demand

We use a lot of some of the fractions, but less of others. From crude oil we get more of some of the less useful fractions and less of some of the more useful ones.

> **Exam tip**
>
> *You do not need to learn details of supply and demand for the fractions, but in an exam you may be given this information and asked questions about it.*

Cracking

A process called **cracking** is used to get more of the fractions we use most. This is carried out at a high temperature, using a catalyst to speed up the reaction.

Most of the hydrocarbons in crude oil belong to a chemical family called **alkanes**. Cracking breaks some of the larger, less useful alkanes to make more of the smaller and more useful ones. This equation shows the cracking of the large alkane decane.

$$C_{10}H_{22} \rightarrow C_8H_{18} + C_2H_4$$
$$\text{decane} \qquad \text{octane} \qquad \text{ethene}$$

Petrol contains octane and other hydrocarbons of similar size, so cracking produces more of the petrol fraction.

In the cracking reaction hydrocarbons belonging to another chemical family, the **alkenes**, are also formed.

These are very useful substances, and are used to make **polymers**. Ethene is used to make poly(ethene), the most widely used polymer.

ethene   poly(ethene)

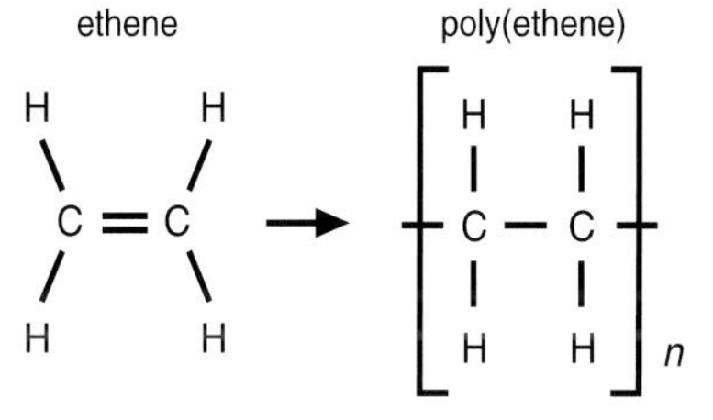

The polymerisation of ethene

Test yourself

1 Fossil fuels are non-renewable sources of energy, but wind power is a renewable source of energy. Explain this difference.

2 Why does an increase in the price of crude oil lead to an increase in the price of many items in shops?

3 Describe the relationship between hydrocarbon molecular size and boiling point shown in the graph.

4 Bitumen is collected at the bottom of the fractionating column. What does this tell you about the hydrocarbon molecules in bitumen?

5 Cracking helps an oil refinery match the supply of its products to the demand for them. Explain how it does this.

C1e Making polymers & C1f Designer polymers

After revising these items you should:

● know how polymers are made and used.

Making polymers

Plastics are made of polymers, which are very large molecules. Polymer molecules are made by joining together lots of small molecules, called **monomers**.

The reaction used to make a polymer from a monomer is called polymerisation, and is carried out at high pressure using a catalyst.

Many polymers are made from alkenes. These are called addition polymers because the monomer molecules add together to make the polymer without forming any other product. During **addition polymerisation** many small **unsaturated** molecules join to form each large **saturated** polymer molecule.

Poly(ethene) is the polymer made by joining together lots of ethene molecules. This polymer is commonly called polythene.

Exam tip

You need to know the formula of methane and ethane.

Alkanes

Crude oil is a mixture of hydrocarbons, which are molecules containing the elements hydrogen and carbon only. Most of the hydrocarbons in crude oil belong to a family called the alkanes. The diagram shows displayed formulae of the first three alkanes.

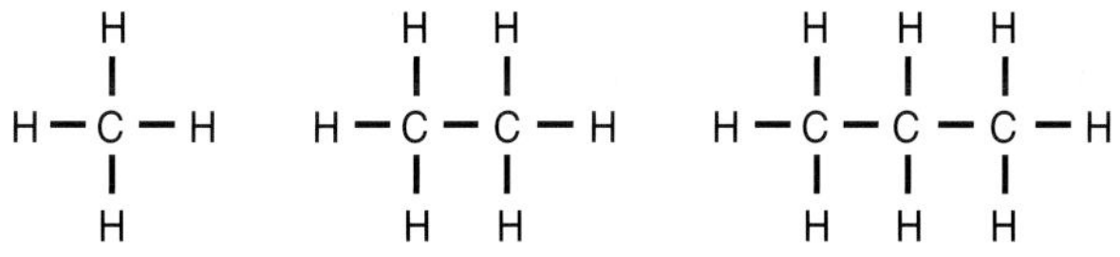

In these molecules hydrogen atoms and carbon atoms share a pair of **electrons** to form a covalent bond. The alkanes are said to be saturated because they contain single covalent bonds only.

Alkenes

The alkenes are another family of hydrocarbons. Alkenes are said to be unsaturated because they have one or more double covalent bonds between carbon atoms. The diagram shows the displayed formulae of two alkenes.

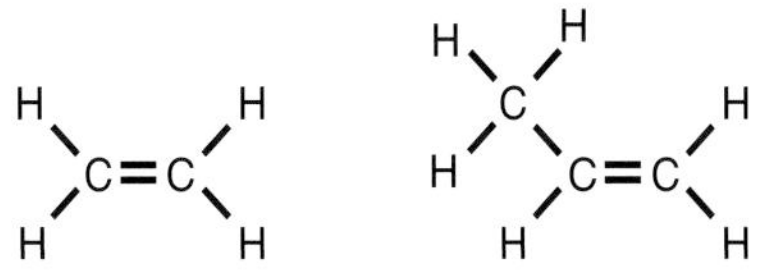

Bromine can be used to test if a compound is saturated or unsaturated.

- When an unsaturated compound such as ethene is bubbled through orange-red bromine water the colour disappears.

- With a saturated compound such as ethane there is no colour change.

The reaction that takes place with ethene is shown in the diagram below.

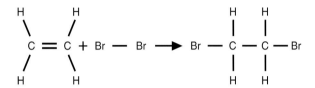

The reaction between ethene and bromine

Designer polymers

Different polymers have different properties. We use a polymer for a particular job because it has the right properties.

The atoms in the polymer chains of plastics are held together by strong covalent bonds. Some plastics have weak intermolecular forces between polymer molecules, so they have low melting points and can be stretched easily.

An example is poly(ethene), which is good for making articles such as plastic bags, buckets and washing up bowls.

Other plastics have strong forces between the polymer molecules. These may be covalent **crosslinking** bridges between adjacent polymer molecules.

These polymers have high melting points, cannot be stretched and are rigid. They are good for making articles that have to withstand high temperatures, such as kettles.

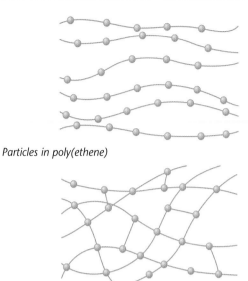

Particles in poly(ethene)

This polymer has links between the polymer chains

Clothing

Outdoor coats may be made of nylon or Gore-Tex®. Nylon is tough, lightweight, waterproof and keeps out UV light. But it does not let water vapour out, so sweat condenses inside the coat. Gore-Tex® is made from nylon laminated with a PTFE/polyurethane membrane.

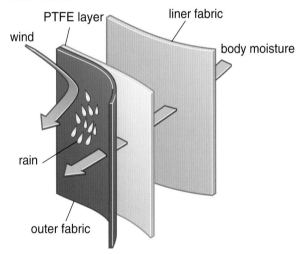

The structure of Gore-Tex®

Holes in the PTFE layer are too small to let water pass through, so rain water cannot get through the coat. The holes are big enough to let water vapour pass through, so sweat can escape as water vapour. This makes the coat waterproof but breathable.

Disposal of polymers

Many polymers, such as poly(ethene), are non-biodegradable. This means that:

- they will not be decomposed or decayed by the action of bacteria
- if they are carelessly thrown away they cause litter
- they can be disposed of in landfill sites, but landfill sites get filled quickly and waste valuable land
- they can be disposed of by burning, but this produces toxic gases.

Both landfill and burning mean that a valuable resource has been wasted.

It is also possible to **recycle** non-biodegradable polymers:

- when a polymer is recycled it can be used again
- but different polymers have to be separately sorted out of the waste, which makes recycling difficult and expensive.

In the future it is likely that many new **biodegradable** polymers will be made.

C1g Using carbon fuels

Choosing the right fuel

We burn fossil fuels to get energy. The amount of fossil fuels we use is increasing as the demand for energy for industry, transport and heating homes increases. Which fuel we use for a particular job depends on a number of factors. The table shows these factors for four fossil fuels.

Complete combustion

A fuel is a substance that reacts with oxygen to release useful energy. This is the process of burning, or **combustion**.

Complete combustion of a hydrocarbon fuel (e.g. petrol):

* requires a plentiful supply of air or oxygen
* releases the maximum amount of energy
* makes only carbon dioxide and water.

We can carry out a simple laboratory demonstration to show that natural gas (methane) is a hydrocarbon fuel.

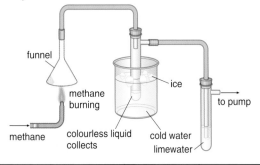

funnel

methane burning

ice

methane

colourless liquid collects

cold water

limewater

to pump

A colourless liquid collects in the tube cooled by the ice. This liquid is water. The limewater goes cloudy, showing that carbon dioxide has been made.
The complete combustion of methane is shown by this equation.

$$CH_4 + 2O_2 \rightarrow CO_2 + 2H_2O$$

methane + oxygen $\rightarrow$ carbon dioxide + water

How science works

A number of years ago, some scientists predicted that carbon dioxide produced by burning fossil fuels would increase the greenhouse effect and so lead to global warming.

Since then measurements have shown that the average annual temperature in many places on the Earth's surface has increased.

What does this suggest about the confidence that we can have in the predictions made by these scientists?

Incomplete combustion

When there is not enough oxygen for a fuel to burn completely, **incomplete combustion** takes place.

Incomplete combustion happens if the fuel does not get a good enough air supply. It gives a cooler yellow flame. This flame contains a lot of soot, which is unburned carbon from the fuel. Carbon monoxide is also produced.

$$4CH_4 + 5O_2 \rightarrow 2CO + 2C + 8H_2O$$

methane + oxygen $\rightarrow$ carbon monoxide + carbon + water

Fuel	Relative cost	Energy value	Availability	Storage	Toxicity	Pollution	Ease of use
coal	cheap	medium	available	easy to store	non-toxic	smoky	difficult to catch alight
oil	expensive	high	widely available	has to be stored in a tank	leaking gas can be poisonous	little pollution	easy to burn
gas from gas main	moderate	high	only in places where there is a gas main	supply directly to house	gas non-toxic; leaks can cause explosion	little pollution	easy to burn
gas in cylinders	expensive	high	widely available	in heavy cylinders	gas non-toxic; leaks can cause explosion	little pollution	easy to burn

When a Bunsen burner air hole is opened complete combustion takes place, giving a hotter blue flame. The blue flame produces more energy than the yellow flame. The blue flame does not produce soot.

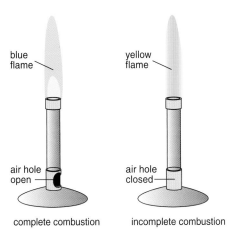

blue flame

yellow flame

air hole open

air hole closed

complete combustion

incomplete combustion

Exam tip

Make sure that you can construct symbol equations for the complete and incomplete combustion of the common fuel gases methane, propane and butane given the formula of the fuel.

Servicing gas fires

When servicing a gas fire or boiler the engineer makes sure that the burning gas has a good supply of air so that complete combustion takes place. In a poor supply of air incomplete combustion takes place. This causes three problems:

- The fire gives out less heat.
- Soot is produced.
- The poisonous gas carbon monoxide is made.

How science works

There are clear advantages in having gas fires and boilers serviced. There are risks involved in not having gas appliances serviced.

Despite this, many people choose not to have their gas appliances serviced. Suggest why.

Test yourself

1 Look at the table on page 36. Which is the best fuel to use in a house in a rural village which does not have a gas main? Explain your choice.

2 Why is the tube that collects liquid water in a complete combustion experiment placed in a beaker of iced water?

3 Propane, C_3H_8, is sold in red cylinders. Write symbol and word equations for the complete combustion of propane.

4 Butane, C_4H_{10}, is sold in blue cylinders. Construct an equation for the incomplete combustion of butane.

5 Why does a blue Bunsen burner flame produce more energy than a yellow Bunsen burner flame?

6 Why might it be dangerous to use a gas fire that has not been serviced for a long time?

C1h Energy

After revising this item you should:

- know about reactions that give out or take in energy.

Exothermic or endothermic

When a piece of magnesium ribbon is dropped into a test tube containing dilute hydrochloric acid:

- a chemical reaction takes place
- the acid bubbles as hydrogen is given off
- the test tube gets hotter
- a thermometer placed in the acid will show an increase in temperature.

The reaction between magnesium and hydrochloric acid is an **exothermic** reaction. During the reaction energy is released.

Some chemical reactions take energy in from the surroundings. If you add solid sodium hydrogencarbonate to a solution of citric acid in a test tube:

- a chemical reaction takes place
- bubbles of carbon dioxide are seen
- the tube feels cold
- a thermometer placed in the mixture will show a decrease in temperature.

The reaction between sodium hydrogencarbonate and citric acid is an **endothermic** reaction. During the reaction energy is taken in.

Bond breaking and bond making

During a chemical reaction, bonds in the **reactants** are broken and new bonds are made in the products.

Energy is needed to break bonds and energy is given out when bonds are formed.

Whether a reaction is exothermic or endothermic depends on the difference between the energy needed to break the bonds of the reactants and the energy given out as the bonds in the **products** are formed.

When methane burns, the bonds in each methane molecule and oxygen molecule are broken.

$$CH_4 + 2O_2 \longrightarrow CO_2 + 2H_2O$$

During the reaction the bonds in each carbon dioxide molecule and water molecule are formed.

Bonds broken: 4 C–H and 2 O=O

Bonds formed: 2 C=O and 4 O–H

In this reaction more energy is released from forming bonds than the energy absorbed from breaking bonds. This excess energy is released as heat into the surroundings. The reaction is exothermic.

Measuring energy changes

The diagram shows a method that can be used to compare the energy transferred in different combustion reactions.

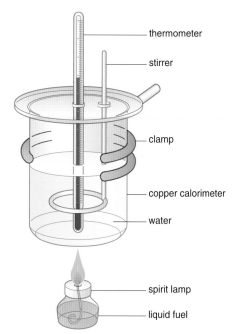

- A measured volume of water is placed in a copper container called a **calorimeter**.
- The water is heated by the combustion of a liquid fuel in a spirit lamp.
- A stirrer is used to make sure that all of the water is at the same temperature.
- A thermometer is used to measure the temperature before and after the liquid fuel is burned.
- The bottle of liquid fuel is weighed before and after the experiment to find how much of the liquid has been burned.

We can use the information from this experiment to calculate the amount of heat released when different liquid fuels are burned. To make this a fair test, the same amount of water is used for each liquid fuel. The heat released is calculated, in joules (J), for the combustion of the same mass of liquid fuel.

The table shows results for an experiment using ethanol in the spirit lamp.

mass of water used	100 g
temperature of water at the start	18°C
temperature of water at the end	32°C
mass of spirit lamp at the start	98.42 g
mass of spirit lamp at the end	96.32 g

The amount of heat energy transferred to the water can be calculated using this formula:

$$\text{energy (J)} = \frac{\text{mass of}}{\text{water (g)}} \times \frac{\text{temperature}}{\text{rise (°C)}} \times 4.2$$

This gives the energy in joules (J), so the answer must be divided by 1000 to be in kilojoules (kJ). This figure is then divided by the mass of fuel burned (in grams) to get the energy output per gram of fuel.

How science works

The energy output calculated from this data is less than the actual energy given out when 1.0 g of ethanol is burned. Suggest why the design of this experiment does not give a more accurate result.

Test yourself

1 When magnesium ribbon is added to dilute hydrochloric acid, what do you see that tells you a chemical reaction is taking place?

2 The reaction between sodium hydrogencarbonate and citric acid is endothermic. What does this tell you about the bonds in the reactants and products in this reaction?

3 Why is it important to stir the water in the calorimeter while the fuel is burning?

4 When experiments are carried out using several different liquid fuels, a different mass of each fuel is burned. But the heat released by each fuel is calculated per g of fuel burned. Why is the heat released calculated in this way?

5 Use the information in the table of results for the experiment using ethanol in the spirit lamp to work out the energy output per gram of ethanol.

6 Similar apparatus can be used to measure the heat released when gaseous or solid fuels are burned. The table below shows a comparison of the heat released by the combustion of some fuels.

Fuel	State of fuel	Energy produced (kJ/g)
hydrogen	gas	243
methane	gas	56
ethanol	liquid	30
petrol	liquid	48

Methane gives out more energy for each 1 g burned than petrol, but most cars are fuelled by petrol rather than methane. Suggest a reason for this.

C2a Paints and pigments & C2b Construction materials

After revising these items you should:

- know about materials used to construct and decorate buildings, including paints and pigments.

Paint ingredients

Paints contain several substances, including a pigment, a solvent and a binding medium. These ingredients are mixed together to form a **colloid**. This is a mixture where solid particles are mixed and dispersed with particles of a liquid, but are not dissolved in the liquid. In paint the solid pigment and binding medium particles are dispersed throughout the liquid solvent particles.

The components of a colloid will not separate because the particles are scattered or dispersed throughout the mixture and are so small that they will not settle out at the bottom.

Paint is applied as a thin layer and the solvent evaporates as the paint dries. Some paints are oil-based, with a hydrocarbon solvent that evaporates quickly. As they dry the oil is oxidised by oxygen in the air to form a hard, durable finish.

Other paints are water-based. They are often called emulsion paints because they are made of a colloid called an emulsion. This contains the pigment and binding agent dispersed through water.

The table shows some properties and uses of these paints.

Paint	Finish	Cleaning of brushes	Uses
oil-based	high gloss	a solvent must be used	indoor and outdoor woodwork
emulsion	matt or satin	can be cleaned in water	indoor walls

Exam tip

A colloid is a mixture of two substances that do not normally mix. There are many examples, such as milk, butter, mayonnaise, smoke.

Dyes

Dyes are used to colour fabrics.

- Some dyes are natural. Most natural dyes are obtained from plants. This means that there is only a limited range of colours available.
- Other dyes are synthetic. These are made in factories. The use of synthetic dyes has increased the number of colours available to colour fabrics.

How science works

The raw materials used to make synthetic dyes are obtained from crude oil. Explain why using natural dyes is more sustainable than using synthetic dyes.

Pigments with special properties

Thermochromic pigments change colour when heated or cooled. They can be used on the outside of electric kettles to show how hot the water is. They can also be used to warn that the liquid in a cup is hot. Thermochromic pigments can be added to acrylic paints to give even more colour changes.

Phosphorescent pigments can glow in the dark. They absorb and store energy and release it as light over a period of time. They can be used to make paints glow in the dark. Paints containing phosphorescent pigments are used to make watch faces that can be seen in the dark. They are much safer than the radioactive substances that were once used for this purpose.

Construction materials

Many **construction materials** are used to build houses and other buildings. Some of these construction materials are made from rocks in the Earth's **crust**. Examples are shown in the table.

Construction material	Source
aluminium	aluminium **ore**
iron	iron ore
brick	clay
cement and **concrete**	limestone, clay, sand, gravel
glass	sand

We can also use rocks themselves as construction materials. Buildings can be made from blocks of:

- **granite**
- limestone
- **marble**

Granite is an **igneous** rock. It is the hardest of these three materials, and will withstand weathering and the wear and tear of daily use.

Limestone and marble are both made of calcium carbonate, but marble is much harder than limestone. Limestone is a sedimentary rock. Marble is a metamorphic rock made by the action of high pressures and high temperatures on limestone. The hardness of a rock depends on how it was formed.

Using limestone

Thermal decomposition is a reaction in which one substance is chemically changed by heating into at least two new substances. When heated strongly, limestone thermally decomposes to make calcium oxide and carbon dioxide.

$CaCO_3$	$\rightarrow$ CaO	+ CO_2
calcium carbonate	$\rightarrow$ calcium oxide	+ carbon dioxide

Exam tip

You should learn the definition of thermal decomposition.

When limestone is heated together with clay, cement is made. We can mix it with sand or gravel and water and the mixture sets to form concrete.

Concrete is very hard but to make it stronger the concrete is set around steel supports to make reinforced concrete. It is a **composite** material because it contains more than one material put together to make a new material.

Reinforced concrete has the hardness of concrete together with the flexibility and strength of steel. This makes it a better construction material than non-reinforced concrete.

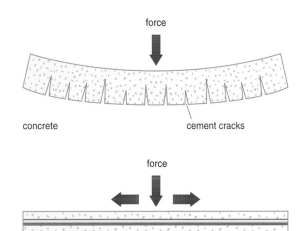

Steel rods make concrete stronger

Test yourself

1. Suggest why outdoor woodwork is painted with oil-based paint rather than emulsion paint.

2. Why do synthetic dyes have more colours than natural dyes?

3. Suggest why phosphorescent paints are safer for watch faces than paints containing radioactive substances.

4. Suggest why marble is harder than limestone.

5. Many tall buildings are made using reinforced concrete. What might happen if steel supports were not put into the concrete?

C2c Does the Earth move?

After revising this item you should:

- know how plate tectonics is changing the appearance of the Earth.

Structure of the Earth

The Earth is a sphere with a thin solid rocky crust, semi-liquid **mantle** and a **core** containing mainly iron. The outer layer of the Earth is cold and rigid, and is called the **lithosphere**. This includes the crust and the outer part of the mantle.

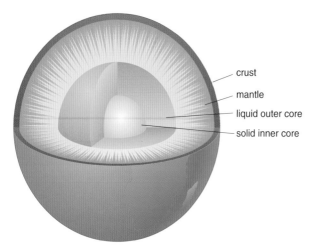

crust
mantle
liquid outer core
solid inner core

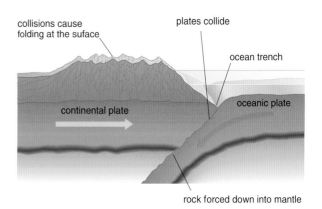

collisions cause folding at the suface
plates collide
ocean trench
continental plate
oceanic plate
rock forced down into mantle

The mantle is the zone between the crust and the core. Deep below the crust the mantle is hot and non-rigid. Here the molten rock, called **magma**, can flow. Just below the core the mantle is cooler and rigid.

The crust is 'cracked' into huge pieces called **tectonic plates**. Oceanic plates lie beneath the oceans and continental plates form the continents. The tectonic plates are less dense than the mantle and float on top of it.

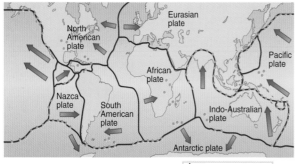

Eurasian plate
North American plate
Pacific plate
African plate
Nazca plate
South American plate
Indo-Australian plate
Antarctic plate

key
→ movement of plate
• earthquake line

Convection currents in the mantle transfer energy to the plates, causing them to move very slowly. In places the oceanic and continental plates collide. Because oceanic plates are more dense than continental plates, as they collide the oceanic plate slides beneath the continental plate. This is called **subduction**, and may result in the partial remelting of tectonic plates.

> **Exam tip**
>
> *Be sure that you know the meaning of key scientific terms such as crust, core, mantle, magma, tectonic plate, subduction zone.*

> **How science works**
>
> In 1915 Alfred Wegener proposed that movement of the plates of the Earth's crust had caused the continents to move away from each other.
>
> At this time there was little evidence to support this theory. His ideas were not accepted by other scientists then, but we now believe that his ideas are correct.
>
> Suggest why scientists changed their views about Wegner's theories.

Volcanoes and igneous rocks

Molten rock, called magma, from the mantle can find its way up through weaknesses in the Earth's crust. Since this magma rises through the crust it shows that the magma is less dense than the crust.

In a **volcano** the magma is forced out onto the surface of the Earth as a stream of **lava**.

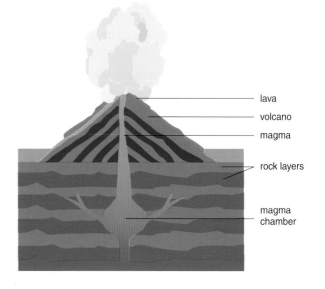

lava
volcano
magma
rock layers
magma chamber

The lava cools quickly to form igneous rock with small crystals. The type of rock formed depends on the composition of the magma that was forced to the surface.

- Iron-rich magma, which is runny and gives lava that runs slowly from the volcano, forms **basalt**.
- Silica-rich magma, which gives lava that is ejected explosively, forms rhyolite.

Explosive eruptions may eject pumice and volcanic ash and bombs, sometimes with graded bedding.

When magma is forced up through cracks in the crust but does not reach as far as the surface, it cools more slowly. This forms igneous rocks with large crystals, such as gabbro and granite.

Exam tip

You need to know how the size of crystals in igneous rocks is related to the rate at which the magma cooled when the rocks were formed.

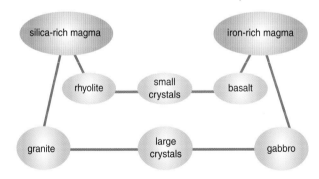

Studying the structure

Studying the structure of the Earth is not easy. Most of our knowledge of the mantle and core has been gained by using instruments. We cannot drill far enough down into the Earth to reach deeper than the upper part of the crust.

We can see magma when it is ejected from volcanoes, though it is hazardous to get near enough to investigate. Geologists study volcanoes to reveal information about the structure of the Earth, but also to enable them to predict future eruptions.

Many people choose to live near volcanoes, often because the soil there is very fertile. They need to be warned if an eruption is about to take place.

How science works

Geologists would like to be able to predict exactly where and when volcanic eruptions and earthquakes will occur, so they study and take measurements of volcanoes and plate movements.

Their predictions are now much better than they were thirty years ago, but they still cannot predict with 100 per cent certainty.

Suggest why.

Test yourself

1 Why may subduction result in the partial remelting of tectonic plates?

2 Volcanoes that eject iron-rich lava are said to be 'safer' than those that eject silica-rich lava. Suggest why.

3 The rocks around a volcano have small crystals. Explain why.

4 Under what conditions does magma cool to form igneous rock with large crystals?

5 How do volcanoes show us that the Earth's crust is denser than the mantle?

C2d Metals and alloys

After revising this item you should:

- know the properties and uses of some metals and alloys.

Copper

The copper extracted from copper ores is pure enough for some uses, such as water pipes. It is not pure enough for making electrical wiring, since impurities increase resistance in the wire.

Impure copper is purified using **electrolysis**. The diagram on the next page shows apparatus for a laboratory demonstration to show this.

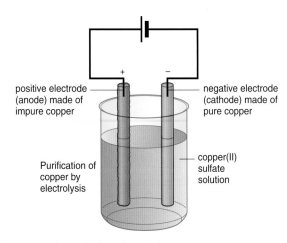

Copper can be purified by electrolysis

The positive electrode (**anode**) is made of impure copper. During electrolysis copper leaves this electrode and is deposited on the negative electrode (**cathode**) which is made of pure copper. The **electrolyte** is copper(II) sulfate solution. Impurities dissolve in this solution or fall to the bottom of the cell.

> **Exam tip**
>
> *You need to remember which electrode is impure copper and which is pure copper. As an aid to remembering this you could say 'I am positive that the copper is not pure', showing that the positive electrode is made of impure copper.*

Recycling copper

Copper is a fairly expensive metal. It is much cheaper to collect and recycle copper that has already been used than to make new copper.

It also saves resources. The Earth has a finite amount of copper ore, and we use a large amount each year. One day we may run out.

There are, however, some problems involved in recycling copper. For example:

- It requires a lot of organisation. Places have to be set up for the used copper to be collected and stored, and people need to be told where these are.
- Most people do not realise the advantage of recycling copper, and simply throw it away. They need to be encouraged to recycle it.

> **How science works**
>
> Explain the advantages of recycling copper instead of extracting it from copper ore.

Alloys

An **alloy** is a mixture of two elements, at least one of which is a metal. Many alloys contain two or more metals mixed together. Examples of alloys are brass, bronze, solder, steel and amalgam. More details about some of these alloys are shown in the table.

Alloy	Main metal	Use
amalgam	mercury	tooth fillings
brass	copper and zinc	hinges, screws, ornaments
solder	lead and tin	joining wires and water pipes

> **Exam tip**
>
> *You need to know which metals are in each of these three alloys.*

Alloy properties

Alloys have properties that are different from those of the metals that they contain. These may make the alloy more useful than the pure metal.

Copper is a fairly soft metal, and reacts with air to form a green coating. Brass is much harder than copper, and is resistant to **corrosion**. This property makes brass more suitable for making hinges and screws than copper.

The table gives details of some properties of the alloy solder, and the metals tin and lead that are mixed together to make it.

Metal	solder	tin	lead
Melting point (°C)	110–130	232	328
Density (g/cm³)	10.3	9.3	11.3
Relative hardness	quite hard	soft	soft

Solder is used to make connections between components in electrical equipment such as radios and computers. Some of these components are damaged at high temperatures.

Smart alloys

Nitinol is an alloy made from nickel and titanium. It has the unusual property of retaining its shape. If you accidentally sit on a pair of spectacles with nitinol frames, they simply spring back into shape.

These **smart alloys** also have military and medical uses. Smart alloys can be used to hold badly fractured bones in place while they heal.

Test yourself

1 The total mass of the apparatus used to purify copper does not change during electrolysis. Suggest why.

2 Copper(II) sulfate solution is blue. Its colour does not change when it is used as an electrolyte during the purification of copper. Explain why.

3 Suggest why only a small proportion of the copper we use is recycled.

4 Steel is a mixture of iron and carbon. How is this mixture different from those in the table of alloys?

5 Suggest why solder is better than lead for making electrical connections in a computer.

C2e Cars for scrap

After revising this item you should:

● know about the metals and alloys used in cars.

Rusting

Iron in contact with water and oxygen forms **rust**. Rusting is an oxidation reaction where iron reacts with water and oxygen to form hydrated iron(III) oxide.

iron + oxygen + water ⟶ hydrated iron(III) oxide

How fast iron rusts depends on the conditions it is in. Salt water and acid rain both speed up the rate of iron rusting.

Iron is the only metal that rusts. Some other metals corrode when exposed to water and oxygen, but aluminium does not. The surface of aluminium has a thin coating of aluminium oxide that protects the metal beneath it from corrosion.

Steel

Steel is an alloy of iron. An alloy is a mixture of two elements, one of which is a metal. Many alloys contain two or more metals mixed together, but to make steel iron is mixed with a very small percentage of carbon, a non-metal.

Like many other alloys, the properties of steel are quite different from those of the metal it is made from.

● Steel is harder than iron.

● Steel is stronger than iron.

● Steel is less likely to corrode than iron.

These properties make steel more useful than iron.

How science works

Scientists tested the hardness of several samples from the same batch of steel. They found that one hardness value was far lower than the others.

Suggest what may have caused this.

Aluminium cars

We can make a car body from aluminium instead of steel. Aluminium has a number of advantages over steel for this use, for example:

● an aluminium car body is lighter than one made of steel, giving better fuel economy

● an aluminium car body will corrode less than a steel body and so may have a longer lifetime.

Aluminium does, however, have one disadvantage:

● A similar car body will be more expensive when made of aluminium rather than steel.

Materials used to make cars

Many materials are used to make a car. We can see this from the pie chart.

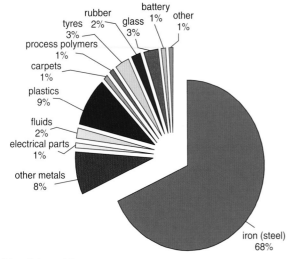

Materials used in cars

Each part of the car is made from a material that has properties that make it suitable for use in that part of the car. For example:

- the body is made of steel because it is strong and can be shaped easily
- seat coverings are made of fibres because they are flexible, durable and can be dyed to give attractive colours
- tyres are made of rubber because it is flexible and hardwearing, but it is strengthened by fibres or steel mesh
- the windscreen is made of glass because it is transparent and scratch resistant.

Recycling metals

We are able to recycle many materials, including some of those used to make cars. There are advantages and problems associated with recycling, as shown in the spider diagram below.

In the United Kingdom it is likely that new laws about materials in cars will soon be passed. These will make sure that a minimum percentage of the materials used to make new cars is recyclable.

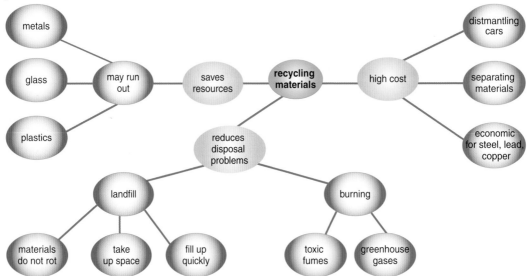

C2f Clean air

After revising this item you should:

- know about the composition of clean air and the gases that pollute it.

Gases in the air

The pie chart shows the composition by volume of clean, dry air. Air also contains a variable amount of water vapour.

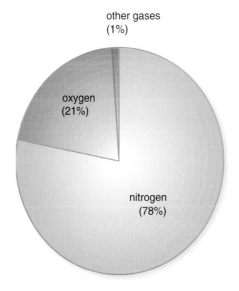

Of the 'other gases', 0.35 per cent is carbon dioxide.

The oxygen, nitrogen and carbon dioxide levels in the air are approximately constant. Processes in the carbon cycle remove and replace both oxygen and carbon dioxide.

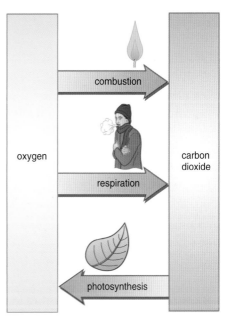

Keeping oxygen and carbon dioxide in balance

During photosynthesis plants remove carbon dioxide from the air and release oxygen into the air. During respiration in plants and animals, and during combustion, oxygen is removed from the air and carbon dioxide is released into the air.

In the carbon cycle these processes balance out, so that the proportion of these two gases in the air does not change.

However, the activities of an increasing population of humans have caused changes in the composition of the air, for example:

- **deforestation** is reducing the amount of carbon dioxide removed by trees
- increased burning of fossil fuels to obtain energy is releasing more carbon dioxide into the air.

Evolution of the atmosphere

The Earth's atmosphere was not always as it is today. The original atmosphere came from gases escaping from the interior of the Earth. This atmosphere contained a lot of carbon dioxide, but no oxygen.

When plants evolved they carried out the process of photosynthesis. This removed carbon dioxide from the air and released oxygen into the air. Gradually the percentage of oxygen in the air increased until it reached today's level.

A theory to explain the evolution of our atmosphere involves several ideas:

1 degassing from the Earth's crust (as gases such as carbon dioxide, steam, ammonia and methane were released from volcanoes)

2 this formed an initial atmosphere of ammonia and carbon dioxide

3 formation of liquid water from steam as the Earth cooled

4 development of photosynthetic organisms that used up carbon dioxide and produced oxygen

5 conversion of ammonia into nitrogen by the action of bacteria

6 this leads to an increase in oxygen and nitrogen levels

7 lack of reactivity of nitrogen resulting in nitrogen remains as the main atmospheric gas due to its lack of reactivity.

Exam tip

You may be asked to describe a theory of how the Earth's atmosphere evolved.

Air pollution

Human activities have released other gases into the air, causing **atmospheric pollution**. The most important of these pollutant gases are shown in the table.

Pollutant	How it forms	Effects
carbon monoxide	incomplete combustion of petrol or diesel in car engines	poisonous gas
oxides of nitrogen	in car engines from the reaction of nitrogen and oxygen	acid rain and photochemical smog
sulfur dioxide	combustion of fossil fuels containing sulfur, for example, coal	acid rain

Exam tip

You may be given information about the effects of atmospheric pollutants and asked to interpret this.

How science works

The table shows measurements of sulfur dioxide made at the side of a busy road. The measurements were made at the same time of day for five consecutive days. Similar measurements were made at the side of a quiet country road.

	Sulfur dioxide concentration ($\mu g/m^3$)				
day	1	2	3	4	5
busy road	81	79	82	80	78
country road	12	10	14	11	13

Obtain a best estimate of the sulfur dioxide **concentration** at each location by working out the mean (average) of each set of five results.

Scientists conclude from these results that sulfur dioxide is being released in car exhaust fumes. How do the results give confidence in this conclusion?

Exam tip

You may be asked to make similar calculations in an exam question.

Reducing air pollution

Pollutant gases are harmful. Acid rain can corrode metals, damage buildings and harm plants and aquatic life. Smog can cause breathing difficulties in humans. It is therefore important that atmospheric pollution is controlled.

The carbon monoxide given out by car engines is very poisonous. By law, all new cars made in the United Kingdom have to be fitted with a catalytic converter. This removes carbon monoxide from the exhaust gases of the car. The catalytic converter changes carbon monoxide into carbon dioxide.

$$2CO + 2NO \rightarrow N_2 + 2CO_2$$

Test yourself

1 Why is the composition of the air given for dry air?

2 Suggest why an increasing human population has an effect on the composition of the air.

3 Suggest why the lack of reactivity of nitrogen is important in the evolution of our atmosphere.

4 Look at the table of pollutant gases. What is similar about the way they are formed?

5 Many scientists believe that an increase in carbon dioxide in the air increases the greenhouse effect and leads to global warming. State and explain the effect that catalytic converters will have on the level of carbon dioxide in the air.

C2g Faster or slower? (1) & C2h Faster or slower? (2)

After revising these items you should:

● know what makes reactions take place at different rates.

Reaction rate

The **rate of a chemical reaction** depends on two things:

● The frequency at which reacting particles collide.

● The energy transferred during the collision.

Increasing reaction rates

The rate of a reaction can be increased by increasing the temperature. At a higher temperature the particles move faster and have more energy, so:

● there are more collisions per second

● each collision has more energy

● the proportion of successful collisions is greater.

This makes the reaction faster.

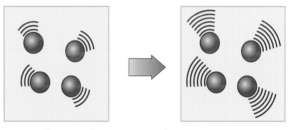

More collisions as the temperature rises

The rate of a reaction can be increased by increasing the concentration of one of the reactants, because:

● at a higher concentration the particles are more crowded

● the particles collide more often.

This makes the reaction faster.

If the reaction involves a gas, increasing the pressure of the gas has the same effect. The higher the pressure, the faster the reaction.

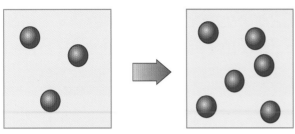

More particles means more collisions

Measuring rate of reaction

We can follow the rate of a reaction by measuring the disappearance of the reactants or the appearance of the products.

When marble chippings (calcium carbonate) and dilute hydrochloric acid react together, carbon dioxide gas is given off. The volume of this gas can be measured at time intervals. This gives a measure of how fast the reaction is going. The solid line on the graph shows the measurements taken during an experiment using this reaction.

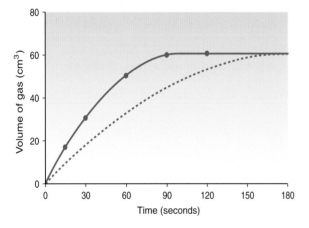

At first the curve rises steeply. The rate of reaction is fast. The concentration of the acid decreases as it is used up in the reaction. This makes the reaction go slower. Eventually all the acid is used up, and the reaction stops. Some marble chippings are left unreacted.

How science works

How could you find out if the data in this graph is reliable?

The reaction is repeated using the same volume of hydrochloric acid but with an equal volume of water added. So the same amount of acid was used, but at half the original concentration. These results are shown by the dotted line on the graph. With a lower concentration the reaction is slower. The dotted line is less steep and takes longer to become horizontal.

The rate of reaction can be calculated at any point by measuring the slope of the graph. The rate is a measure of volume divided by time.

Exam tip

You will be expected to be able to calculate a rate of reaction from a graph or figures in a table. It is worth practising this skill.

Catalysts

A catalyst is a substance that changes the rate of a reaction but is unchanged at the end of the reaction. Because it is not used up during the reaction, only a small amount of catalyst is needed to catalyse large amounts of reactants. The catalyst makes the reaction go quicker, but does not affect the quantity of the products made. A catalyst is often specific to a particular reaction.

When hydrogen peroxide decomposes, oxygen gas is released. This reaction is catalysed by solid manganese(IV) oxide. The graph shows the volume of oxygen gas given off during a reaction using 25 cm³ of hydrogen peroxide and 0.2 g of manganese(IV) oxide.

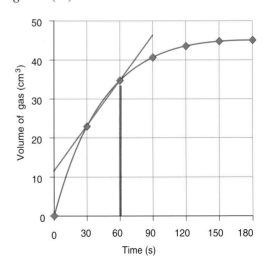

Surface area

For reactions that involve a solid, the rate of reaction is also affected by the size of the solid lumps used. The graph below shows the results of two experiments carried out at the same temperature, using the same mass of marble (calcium carbonate) and the same volume and concentration of hydrochloric acid. In one experiment powdered marble is used and in the other a lump of marble.

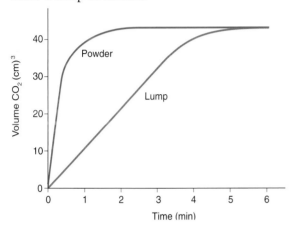

The red line is steeper than the green line, and this reaction is finished in a shorter time, showing that the powder reacted faster than the lump. For the same mass, the powder has a larger surface area than the lump. This is shown in the diagram.

If the limestone is crushed, the surface area is bigger because more surface is exposed

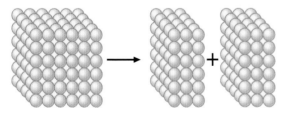

In each case, the acid particles collide with the limestone more frequently, and so the reaction will get faster

Because the powder has more surface area than the lump, the frequency of collisions with particles of acid is greater. This results in a faster reaction.

Exam tip

Make sure that you can explain why changes in temperature, concentration and surface area cause changes in rate of reaction.

Exploding custard

An **explosion** is a very fast reaction which releases a large volume of gaseous products. If a fine powder of a combustible solid is mixed with air, and a flame applied, an explosion may result. This can happen with solids such as coal dust, flour and even custard. Care has to be taken in coal mines, flour mills and custard factories to prevent a build up of dust in the air.

How science works

Even though care is taken, explosions sometimes happen in coal mines. Miners are in danger of injury from these explosions. Despite this danger, large quantities of coal are still mined.

Suggest why this is.

Test yourself

1 Explain why, in a reaction involving gases, increasing pressure increases the rate of reaction.

2 Look at the graph for the reaction rate investigation (page 50). When is the rate of reaction highest?

3 Explain why both reactions produce the same final volume of carbon dioxide.

4 Calculate the rate of the reaction shown by the solid line between 30 and 60 seconds.

5 Sketch a graph to show how the rate of this reaction would change if it was carried out at a higher temperature.

6 Look at the graph for the catalyst investigation (page 50). What total volume of oxygen was collected when the reaction had finished?

7 How can you tell from the graph that the reaction is faster after 30 s than it is after 60 s?

8 Comment on, and give an explanation for, the amount of product formed in the two reactions of the surface area investigation.

9 Copy the graph of reaction times above left and sketch on it the results you would expect using several smaller lumps of marble. (The total mass is unchanged.)

P1a Heating houses

Temperature and heat

Temperature is a measure of how hot or cold an object is on a chosen scale. Temperature is measured in degrees Celsius (°C).

Heat is a measurement of energy on an absolute scale. Heat is measured in joules (J).

The temperature of different parts of an object can be shown using a **thermogram**. The hotter parts appear red, the colder parts appear blue.

Energy flow

Heat energy always flows from a hotter object to a cooler one. The hotter an object is the faster the rate at which it loses heat energy.

● An object that is hotter than its surroundings will lose heat energy and cool down.

● An object that is cooler than its surroundings will gain heat energy and warm up.

Specific heat capacity

The amount of energy needed to change the temperature of an object depends on:

● its mass

● the material it is made from

● the size of the temperature change.

Equal masses of different materials need different amounts of energy for the same temperature change.

The **specific heat capacity** of a material is:

● the energy needed to raise the temperature of 1 kg of the material by 1°C.

The units of specific heat capacity are joules per kilogram per degree Celsius (J/kg/°C).

The greater the specific heat capacity of a material the more energy it can hold.

The equation for this is:

$$\text{energy (J)} = \text{mass (kg)} \times \text{specific heat capacity (J/kg/°C)} \times \text{temperature change (°C)}$$

Melting and boiling

Melting is changing from solid into liquid, boiling is changing from liquid into gas. These changes are called changes of **state** and energy is needed to make them happen.

Different materials melt and boil at different temperatures. While a material is melting or boiling there is no change in temperature because the energy being supplied is used to overcome the forces of attraction between particles in the solid or liquid, breaking the intermolecular bonds.

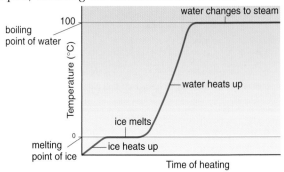

The graph shows what happens when ice is heated until it first becomes water, and then the water becomes steam. The horizontal parts of the graph show that:

● the temperature stays at 0°C while the ice melts

● and it stays at 100°C while the water changes to steam.

Specific latent heat

The **specific latent heat** of a material is:

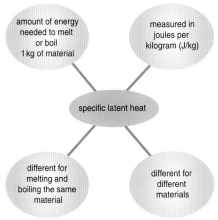

The equation for specific latent heat is:

energy (J) = mass (kg) × specific latent heat (J/kg)

Freezing

Freezing is changing from liquid into solid, such as from water to ice. When a material freezes it loses energy, but there is no change in temperature.

Test yourself

1 Calculate the energy required to raise the temperature of 3 kg of water from 10°C to 20°C. The specific heat capacity of water is 4200 J/kg/°C.

2 In an experiment a block of iron is heated to 125°C and left to cool to 25°C. As it cools it gives out 88 000 J of heat energy. The mass of the block is 2 kg. What is the specific heat capacity of iron?

3 Why does adding ice at 0°C cool your drink more than adding water at 0°C?

4 A student adds some ice to a drink. The ice all melts as 9900 J of energy is transferred to it from the drink. The specific latent heat of ice is 330 000 J/kg. Calculate the mass of ice the student added to the drink.

5 Why is a burn from steam at 100°C likely to be worse than a burn from water at 100°C?

P1b Keeping homes warm & P1c How insulation works

After revising these items you should:

- be able to compare the payback time of different types of insulation, explain what is meant by conduction, convection and radiation and how we can reduce heat loss by these processes.

Saving money

Reducing the heat energy losses from a house saves the householder money on fuel bills. Any energy-saving features added by the householder will cost money to install. A way of working out the cost-effectiveness of these features is called the **payback time**.

$$\text{payback time (years)} = \frac{\text{installation cost (£)}}{\text{fuel saving (£ per year)}}$$

Efficiency

The **efficiency** of a system tells you how much of the energy that goes into that system is usefully transferred. The rest of the energy is wasted.

You can calculate efficiency using the equation:

$$\text{efficiency} = \frac{\textbf{useful energy output}}{\textbf{total energy input}}$$

Transfer of heat energy

Heat energy is transferred by:

- **conduction**
- **convection**
- **radiation**

An energy efficient home reduces the transfer of energy by each of these processes. This means that less energy is wasted and the householder saves money.

Conduction

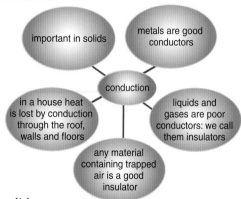

- important in solids
- metals are good conductors
- conduction
- in a house heat is lost by conduction through the roof, walls and floors
- liquids and gases are poor conductors: we call them insulators
- any material containing trapped air is a good insulator

In a solid:

- the particles are held together by strong forces, but vibrate continuously about fixed positions
- heating one end of a solid gives the particles more **kinetic energy** so they vibrate more.

This causes neighbouring particles to vibrate more, and in this way kinetic energy is passed between the particles.

In liquids and gases:

- the forces between particles are weaker than in solids
- the particles are able to move around and energy does not easily pass from particle to particle as in solids.

Air is a poor conductor so materials that contain air, such as glass fibre, are good insulators.

Convection

When a gas is heated it expands, becomes less dense and rises. This change of density causes fluid flow as the rising warm gas is replaced by falling colder gas, which has a higher density.

In this way a convection current is set up that transfers heat through the gas. Convection also takes place in liquids, for the same reason.

Exam tip

You must be able to explain convection currents in terms of different densities. Warm air rises because it has a lower density; cold air sinks because it has a higher density. It is not enough to say simply 'hot air rises' and 'cold air falls'.

Cavity walls reduce energy loss by conduction, but as the air inside them flows, heat is lost by convection instead. We can reduce this heat loss by adding cavity wall insulation, which traps the air in pockets, preventing convection.

Radiation

All objects lose heat energy through waves called **infrared** radiation. This radiation does not need a medium to travel through and is the way that heat energy from the Sun reaches us through space.

Light, shiny surfaces reflect infrared radiation. A layer of shiny foil placed on a wall behind a heater reflects infrared radiation back into the room. This reduces energy loss through the wall. Painting the outside walls of a house white also reduces energy loss by radiation as light, shiny surfaces are poor emitters of radiation.

Exam tip

In explaining how a particular method of reducing heat loss works, make sure you explain which type(s) of heat loss it reduces.

Test yourself

1 Why does a stone floor feel colder to your feet than a carpet?

2 Cavity wall insulation costs £800 to install and saves £200 per year on fuel. A porch costs £700 to install and saves £150 per year. Which has the shorter payback time?

3 Why are hot water tanks often covered with a jacket made from glass fibre?

4 For every 100 J of energy supplied to a gas central heating system 92 J are usefully transferred as heat. Calculate the efficiency of the system.

5 An electric fan heater has an efficiency of 0.96.

  (a) Calculate the useful heat energy output produced by the heater when 50 J of electrical energy are input.

  (b) Suggest what happens to the energy that is not usefully transferred as heat in the fan heater.

6 Explain why two walls with an air-filled cavity between them are more effective at reducing heat loss than a single wall.

7 Explain why filling the cavity between two walls with foam or polystyrene beads is more effective at reducing heat loss than an air-filled cavity.

8 Explain why wearing white clothes in a hot country will keep you cooler than wearing black clothes.

P1d Cooking with waves & P1e Infrared signals

After revising these items you should:

- be able to explain some applications of infrared radiation and microwaves and the advantages of using digital signals.

Cooking with infrared

Infrared radiation is the heat source in toasters, cookers and grills. The infrared radiation is absorbed by all particles on the surface of the food, increasing their kinetic energy, and this increases the temperature of the food. The energy is transferred to the centre of the food by conduction or convection.

Infrared radiation is reflected by shiny surfaces such as tin foil.

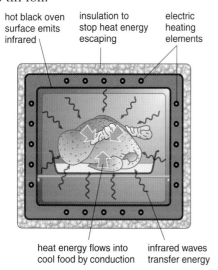

hot black oven surface emits infrared

insulation to stop heat energy escaping

electric heating elements

heat energy flows into cool food by conduction

infrared waves transfer energy

Cooking with microwaves

Microwaves can also be used for cooking:

- The microwaves produced in a microwave oven penetrate about 1 cm into the food. They are absorbed by water molecules in the outside layers of the food, increasing their kinetic energy and raising the temperature of the food.

- The energy is transferred to the centre of the food from the outside by conduction or convection.

- Microwaves pass through glass and plastic but are reflected by metal, so most of the microwaves stay inside the oven.

The water in body tissue will absorb microwaves and the heat released can cause burns.

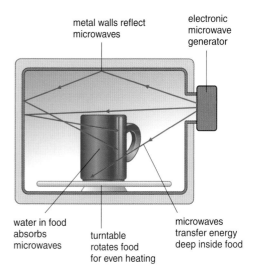

metal walls reflect microwaves

electronic microwave generator

water in food absorbs microwaves

turntable rotates food for even heating

microwaves transfer energy deep inside food

Energy in waves

Like infrared radiation and visible light, microwaves are part of the electromagnetic spectrum. Different radiations in this spectrum have different properties and uses but they all travel as waves, carrying energy through empty space.

The amount of energy carried by an electromagnetic wave depends on its **frequency**. The higher the frequency, the greater the energy and the more dangerous the radiation. Visible light has a higher frequency than infrared radiation, which has a higher frequency than microwaves.

Microwaves and mobile phones

Mobile phones use microwave signals which are transmitted first between the mobile phone and a mobile phone mast, and then between masts.

The microwaves can carry information over long distances provided that they are in 'line of sight'. This is because microwaves cannot bend round corners or over mountains. Places that are not in line of sight with a mast will get a poor signal.

Over long distances the signal may become weakened by interference or **diffraction**, so the transmitters are placed fairly close together and high up away from obstacles.

As the microwaves from your mobile phone pass through your brain they heat it up slightly. Some people are concerned that the use of mobile phones may cause brain tumours, and they may be a particular danger to young children.

Mobile phone masts emit much more radiation than a mobile phone. Many people are concerned about masts placed in their communities.

So far it has not been proved that the masts are harmful. However, this may change as further research is carried out.

Analogue and digital signals

Two types of signal are used to transmit data, **analogue** and **digital**.

- Analogue signals have a continuously variable value.

- Digital signals are either on (1) or off (0).

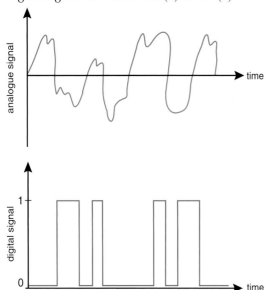

Digital signals allow much more information to be transmitted because many signals can be interleaved on the same data line without interfering with each other. This is called **multiplexing**.

All signals weaken as they travel and need to be amplified. When an analogue signal is amplified any noise (unwanted signals) is also amplified and this causes distortion. When a digital signal is amplified any noise is removed beforehand and is not amplified.

Total internal reflection

A ray of light travelling in a transparent material, such a water, glass or perspex, is **refracted** (changes direction) when it reaches a boundary. The ray only passes out of the material if the angle of incidence is less than the **critical angle**.

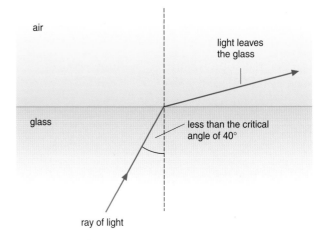

If the angle of incidence is the same as the critical angle the light travels along the surface. If the angle of incidence is greater than the critical angle **total internal reflection** takes place.

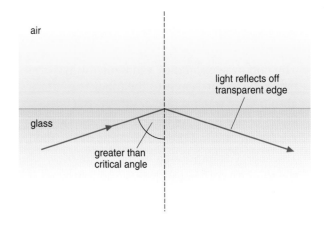

Optical fibres

Infrared or visible light signals are used to transmit data very rapidly along **optical fibres**.

Here are some properties of optical fibres:

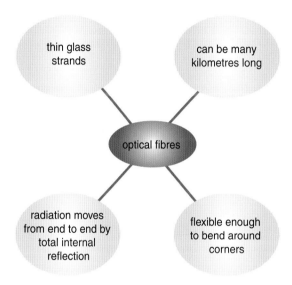

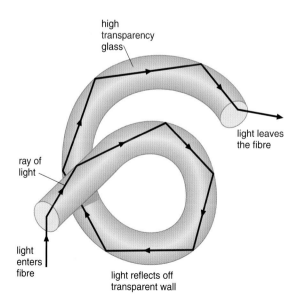

P1f Wireless signals

Uses of wireless technology

The uses of **wireless technology** include:

● radio

● mobile phones

● connecting laptop computers to the Internet.

Refraction

Electromagnetic waves change direction when they cross the boundary from one material into another. This is called refraction.

The change in direction occurs because the waves change speed as they cross the boundary. The speed of the wave depends on the material it is passing through.

Radio waves are refracted as they pass through layers of air of different densities in the Earth's atmosphere. This allows them to bend around the curve of the Earth's surface.

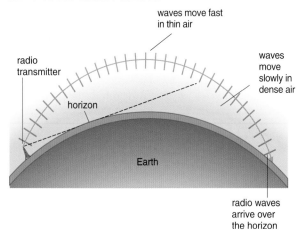

Exam tip

*Remember that when a wave moves from one material into another its speed and **wavelength** change, but its frequency stays the same.*

Radio transmissions

Radio stations broadcast their signals from transmitter masts to radio stations in our homes. If you are a long distance from the mast the signal you receive will be weak and you will not be able to hear the radio programme clearly. The mast has to be positioned above your horizon to provide you with a good signal.

The transmitter mast emits lots of different frequencies of radio waves at once. Each radio station is allocated its own set of **transmission frequencies**, so you tune your radio to a particular frequency to receive a particular station. This reduces interference – picking up unwanted signals from other stations.

Long distance radio transmissions

Radio waves used for long distance transmissions can be reflected off a charged layer in the upper atmosphere called the **ionosphere**.

We can also achieve long distance transmissions using microwaves (the shortest of the radio waves). These:

- travel in straight lines
- pass through the Earth's atmosphere
- are received by a **satellite** in a geostationary **orbit**
- are retransmitted to another receiver on the Earth.

Diffraction

Diffraction is the spreading out of waves when they pass through a gap or around an obstacle. The effect is most noticeable when the size of the gap or obstacle is similar to the wavelength of the wave.

The dish on a transmitter collects the waves and sends them into space.

- If the diameter of the dish is similar to the wavelength of the waves diffraction occurs, the waves spread as they travel and some of the signal is lost.
- If the diameter of the dish is much larger than the wavelength of the waves the signal does not spread out, so a stronger signal is produced.

Exam tip

Make sure that you can explain the difference between reflection, refraction and diffraction.

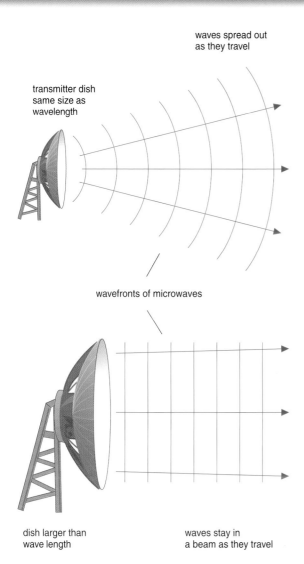

transmitter dish
same size as
wavelength

waves spread out
as they travel

wavefronts of microwaves

dish larger than
wave length

waves stay in
a beam as they travel

Digital radio

This table compares the properties of analogue and digital radio:

Analogue	Digital
A separate set of frequencies. This limits the number of stations that can operate in each area.	Uses digital coding. This results in better reception with less noise or interference.
In some places reflected and direct signals may interfere, giving a poor quality signal.	Each station has the same channel all over the country, so there is no need to retune.
Each station has a different channel in different areas, so if you are travelling you have to retune to keep a clear signal.	Many different stations can broadcast in each area.

P1g Light

Electromagnetic waves

Electromagnetic waves are **transverse waves**.

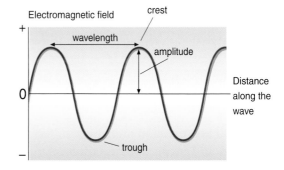

A transverse wave consists of **crests** and **troughs**.

- The **amplitude** of a transverse wave is the height of a crest.
- The **wavelength** is the distance from one crest to the next.
- The unit of wavelength is metres (m).
- The frequency is the number of waves per second.
- The unit of frequency is hertz (Hz).

Wave equation

The speed, wavelength and frequency of a wave are related by the equation

wave speed (m/s) = frequency (Hz) × wavelength (m)

All electromagnetic waves travel at the same high speed through the vacuum of space. This speed is sometimes called the 'speed of light' and is 300 000 000 m/s.

Morse code

Historical communications systems used light or electrical signals to carry messages as fast as the light or electrical signal could travel. This required the use of codes.

One well-known code is the **Morse code**, which uses dots and dashes to represent letters. It was first used to send messages through wires by pulsing the current in them on and off. It can also be used with a signal lamp or torch that is switched on and off to produce pulses of light.

Pulses of light are now used in many communications systems to transfer information.

Light, radio and electrical signals

These signals can all be used as means of communication:

- Light in optical fibres.
- Radio waves.
- Electrical pulses in wires.

They all carry information at the same speed, literally the 'speed of light'.

However, the amount of information they can carry varies: it depends on the frequency of the wave. Since light has a much higher frequency than radio waves it can carry much more information per second.

Another advantage of light is that it is not affected by magnetic and electric fields, but radio and electrical signals are.

The advantage of radio signals is that they are sent through the air without needing a connection, but light signals need to be sent down optical fibres and electrical signals require connecting wires.

Lasers

A **laser** produces an intense beam of light in which all of the waves are:

- the same frequency
- in phase with each other.

Lasers are used to read the information stored on a compact disc (CD). The information is stored as a digital code consisting of a series of pits in the surface of a plastic disc. Laser light reflects from the shiny surface (which contains digital information) of the disc onto a detector. This is read as a 1. Each time a pit passes under the laser the amount of light reflected decreases and this is read as a 0.

Lasers are also used:

- to send light down optical fibres
- to read bar codes on products in supermarkets.

Test yourself

1. What is meant by the frequency of a wave?
2. What is the speed of a wave with a frequency of 19 Hz and a wavelength of 10 mm? Include an appropriate unit with your answer.
3. A wave has a speed of 96 m/s and a wavelength of 8 cm. Calculate the frequency of the wave.
4. Suggest one advantage of using wires instead of light to send messages in Morse code.
5. Why can light signals carry more information than radio signals?

P1h Stable Earth

After revising this item you should:

- be able to explain some effects of ultraviolet radiation on the skin, describe how seismic waves can be used to provide evidence for the structure of the Earth and explain some reasons for climate change.

Earthquakes

The energy released by an **earthquake** travels through the Earth as seismic shock waves. These waves can cause enormous damage. They can be detected and measured by devices called seismometers.

There are two types of seismic waves: **P-waves** and **S-waves**.

P-waves	S-waves
longitudinal waves travel faster than S-waves travel through solids and liquids	transverse waves travel slower than P-waves only travel through solids

P-waves can travel through solid rock and liquid rock, so they can travel through all layers of the Earth. S-waves cannot travel through the liquid outer core.

By comparing the time difference between P-waves and S-waves arriving at seismic measuring stations located at different points on the Earth's surface, scientists have been able to construct a theory of the structure of the Earth.

Exam tip

*Remember that **S**-waves travel **s**lower than P-waves. After an earthquake, P-waves arrive at a seismic measuring station first.*

Ultraviolet radiation

Ultraviolet radiation is part of the electromagnetic spectrum. The Earth receives ultraviolet radiation from the Sun. Ultraviolet radiation has a higher frequency than visible light and carries more energy.

Darker skins are at less risk of damage from ultraviolet radiation because they absorb more of the radiation in the top layers, so less reaches the live skin cells below the surface.

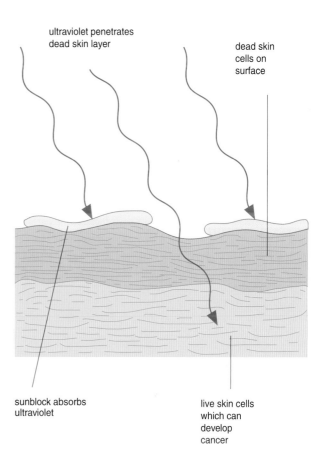

ultraviolet penetrates dead skin layer

dead skin cells on surface

sunblock absorbs ultraviolet

live skin cells which can develop cancer

Sun blocks absorb ultraviolet radiation and so protect the skin. The **sun protection factor**, SPF, indicates how long you can expect to stay in the sun without burning. For example an SPF of 10 indicates you can stay in the sun without burning for 10 times longer than without protection.

Ozone layer

The ozone layer, high up in the Earth's atmosphere, absorbs much of the ultraviolet radiation from the Sun, stopping it reaching the Earth.

There is evidence that artificial chemicals called CFCs are destroying this layer. If this is the case more ultraviolet radiation will reach the surface of the Earth. This is likely to increase the incidence of skin cancer.

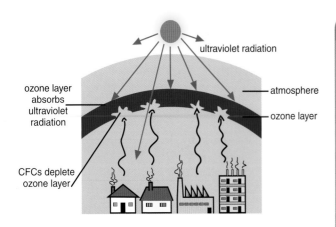

ultraviolet radiation

ozone layer absorbs ultraviolet radiation

atmosphere

ozone layer

CFCs deplete ozone layer

How science works

Scientists have shown strong links between exposure to ultraviolet radiation and skin cancer. Effective sun protection products have been developed, yet still many people continue to sunbathe without protecting their skin.

Exam tip

Remember that the higher the frequency of electromagnetic radiation the more energy it carries and the more dangerous it is.

Climate change

The Earth absorbs infrared and light radiation from the Sun, heating it. The Earth emits infrared radiation into space, cooling it.

Climate changes can come about as a result of both natural events and human activity:

- Dust from volcanoes reflects electromagnetic radiation from the Sun, which causes cooling.
- Dust from factories reflects electromagnetic radiation from cities back down to Earth, causing warming.
- The increased burning of fossil fuels to provide energy puts carbon dioxide into the atmosphere. This stops infrared radiation escaping from the Earth and causes warming.
- Burning forests also increases the amount of carbon dioxide in the atmosphere and causes warming.

Test yourself

1   Give two ways in which P-waves are different from S-waves.

2   How does the destruction of the ozone layer increase the risk of skin cancer?

3   Someone who normally burns after 12 minutes in the Sun applies a sunblock with an SPF of 15. How long could they now stay in the Sun without getting burned?

4   How may global warming result in the extinction of some plants and animals?

5   The graph shows how global temperatures have changed since 1860.

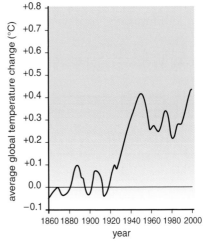

(a)   What was the average global temperature change in 1860?

(b)   What was the average global temperature change in 2000?

(c)   The rate of average global temperature change has increased between 1860 and 2000. Use the graph to help you describe this increase.

(d)   Suggest and describe one natural phenomenon that may have caused this increase.

(e)   Suggest and describe one human activity that may have caused this increase.

P2a Collecting energy from the Sun

After revising this item you should:

● be able to explain some uses of solar energy and wind power, and their advantages and disadvantages.

Photocells

One way of making use of energy from the Sun (solar energy) is with a **photocell**. This transfers light energy into electrical energy as follows:

1 Light falls on the silicon crystals in the photocell.

2 This gives enough energy to the electrons in the silicon to separate them from the atoms.

3 The electrons can then move freely.

4 If connected to a circuit the electrons will flow as an electrical current, transferring energy as they do so.

Photocells produce **direct current** (DC). This is electric current that flows in the same direction all the time.

The amount of electrical energy produced per second, the **power**, depends on:

● the surface area of the photocell that is exposed to light

● the intensity of the light.

Single photocells are used to power devices such as watches and calculators. If a large amount of power is required, many photocells are linked together.

Pros and cons of photocells

There are many advantages to using photocells:

Disadvantages include:

● The conversion of light energy into electrical energy only takes place in sunlight (or thin cloud cover) – no power is produced at night or if the weather is very bad.

● Single cells only produce small amounts of power.

Sometimes photocells are used to charge a battery. This transfers the electrical energy to chemical energy so it can be stored. We can then use the battery to power electrical devices when it is dark.

How science works

Photocells can be used to produce power where there is no mains supply but plenty of sunlight, such as in remote villages in hot countries.

They are also used to power satellites in space where a power supply is needed, but taking fuel or enough batteries from Earth would increase the weight of the satellite.

Solar heating

Some houses have passive solar heating. It works like this:

1 A glass wall is built on the sunny side of the house (usually the south side) with a space between it and the house wall.

2 Glass is transparent to light, so sunlight passes through the glass and is absorbed by the wall, which re-emits the energy as infrared radiation.

3 The infrared radiation is reflected by the glass and heats the surrounding air.

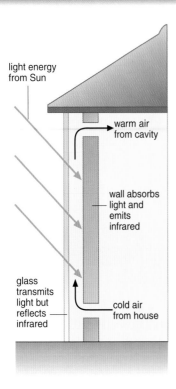

light energy from Sun

warm air from cavity

wall absorbs light and emits infrared

glass transmits light but reflects infrared

cold air from house

Solar cooking

Sunlight falling on a curved mirror is reflected and can be focused on an object such as a cooking pot. The pot absorbs the light energy and heats up, cooking the food inside.

For the device to be efficient the position of the mirror must be adjusted to track the position of the Sun in the sky so the light stays focused in the correct place.

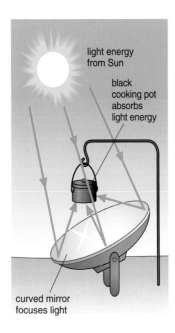

light energy from Sun

black cooking pot absorbs light energy

curved mirror focuses light

Wind power

Heat energy from the Sun creates convection currents in the air around us, making the air move as winds. The moving air has kinetic energy (KE). Devices called wind turbines are used to transfer the kinetic energy to electrical energy.

There are advantages and disadvantages to using **wind turbines** to generate electricity:

Advantages	Disadvantages
use a renewable energy source	their output is dependent on the wind speed
are tough	many are needed to produce the same output as a conventional power station, taking up lots of space
do not produce waste pollution	produce visual and noise pollution

Test yourself

1. Why can solar energy be called a 'renewable' energy resource?

2. What is the energy transfer that takes place in a photocell?

3. A student is investigating photocells. She wants to know how the voltage produced by a set of photocells depends on the surface area exposed to sunlight. She measures the voltage with a voltmeter.

   (a) Suggest how the student could vary the amount of light reaching the photocells.
   (b) What should she do to make her results reliable?
   (c) What variable must the student try and keep the same to ensure a fair test?

4. Why are many wind turbines needed to produce the same output as a conventional power station?

5. Wind farms are often sited in remote locations on hilltops and on the coast. Suggest why.

P2b Generating electricity

After revising this item you should:

- be able to explain how electricity is generated in a power station, calculate the efficiency of this process and explain how electricity is distributed using the National Grid.

The dynamo effect

If a magnet is moved past a coil of wire, or a coil of wire is moved past a magnet, a voltage is produced across the ends of the wire. If the wire is part of a complete circuit a current will flow. We call this the **dynamo effect**.

You can increase the size of the voltage (and current) by:

- using a stronger magnet
- increasing the number of turns on the coil
- moving the magnet or the coil faster.

Exam tip

Be careful in the exam: using a stronger magnet is not the same as using a bigger magnet.

Generator

In a simple **generator** a magnet spins inside a coil of wire wound on an iron core. As the magnet spins it changes the **magnetic field** in the iron core, producing a voltage across the ends of the coil.

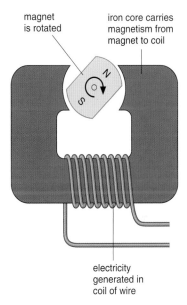

magnet is rotated

iron core carries magnetism from magnet to coil

electricity generated in coil of wire

A generator can also be made by spinning a coil of wire inside a stationary magnetic field.

A generator produces **alternating current** (AC). The direction of the voltage continuously changes so the direction of the current continuously changes. The number of cycles per second is called the frequency of the AC.

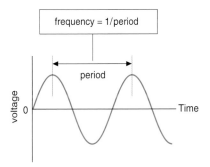

frequency = 1/period

period

voltage

Time

Power stations

Many power stations burn fuel, such as coal, oil or gas, to produce heat. This is used to turn water into steam. The steam passes through a turbine, forcing it to spin. The shaft of the turbine is connected to a generator, which turns and produces electricity.

In many power stations much of the energy from the burning fuel is wasted in heating the surroundings.

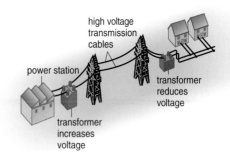

Efficiency

For a power station

fuel energy input	=	waste energy output	+	electrical energy output

The efficiency of a power station can be calculated using the equation

$$\text{efficiency} = \frac{\text{electrical energy output}}{\text{fuel energy input}}$$

The National Grid

All the electricity produced in power stations in the UK is fed into a system called the **National Grid**. This is a network of cables that links power stations to consumers such as homes, schools, shops, offices, factories and farms.

Electricity is transmitted across the National Grid at a very high voltage. For any given power, increasing the voltage decreases the current. This reduces the heating of the cables, and so decreases energy waste. The voltage is increased to several hundred thousand volts by step-up **transformers**.

It would be dangerous to supply electricity to consumers at these very high voltages, so the voltage is reduced to 230 volts by a step-down transformer before it reaches consumers.

This flow chart summarises the stages in the production of electricity.

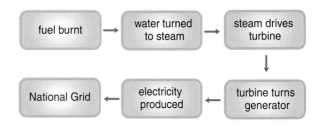

Test yourself

1 The magnet in a generator is spun faster. Describe what happens to the output voltage of the generator.

2 A power station produces 300 J of electrical energy for each 1000 J of energy obtained from the fuel it burns. What is the efficiency of the power station?

3 A power station has an efficiency of 0.5. How much fuel must be input for every 100 J of electrical energy output?

4 Why is the National Grid a better way to supply electricity than having a particular power station for each area?

5 Explain why electricity is transmitted across the National Grid at very high voltages.

P2c Fuels for power

- be able to compare the advantages and disadvantages of common energy sources used in power stations, understand how energy is released from them and calculate the power of and energy used by an appliance.

Heat energy from fuels

The heat energy required to turn water to steam in a power station can be supplied in a number of different ways:

- Fossil fuels such as coal, crude oil and natural gas can be burned.
- Renewable **biomass** such as wood, straw and manure can be burned.
- **Uranium** atoms can be split into smaller atoms, releasing heat in a nuclear power station.
- Biomass can be fermented to produce methane gas, which can be burned.

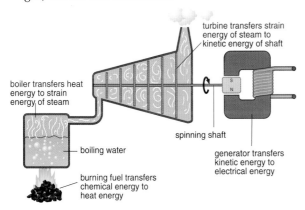

turbine transfers strain energy of steam to kinetic energy of shaft

boiler transfers heat energy to strain energy of steam

boiling water

burning fuel transfers chemical energy to heat energy

spinning shaft

generator transfers kinetic energy to electrical energy

The table shows the pros and cons of using fossil fuels:

Advantages	Disadvantages
reliable source of energy	non-renewable source of energy
do not depend on the weather or the time of the day to produce electricity	burning fossil fuels releases carbon dioxide, a greenhouse gas
gas power stations can be started up quickly at times of sudden demand	burning coal and oil releases sulfur dioxide, producing acid rain

Exam tip

Exam questions often ask for advantages and disadvantages of different energy sources. Make sure that you give both. There are disadvantages associated with all energy resources, even the renewable ones.

Power

The amount of electrical energy that an appliance uses depends on:

- its power
- the length of time it is switched on.

The power of an appliance is usually given on the appliance. Or it can be calculated using the equation:

$$\text{power (W)} = \text{voltage (V)} \times \text{current (A)}$$

The unit of power is the **watt** (W), or the **kilowatt** (kW).

$$1\,kW = 1000\,W$$

Paying for electricity

Companies that supply mains electricity charge customers for the amount of electrical energy used. This is measured in **kilowatt-hours** (kWh). A kilowatt-hour is:

- the amount of energy that is transferred by a one kilowatt device when used for one hour.

You can calculate the energy used by an appliance, in kilowatt-hours, using the equation:

$$\text{energy (kWh)} = \text{power (kW)} \times \text{time used (hours)}$$

The electricity meter in a house records the number of kilowatt-hours of energy used. The energy used between readings is found by subtracting the previous meter reading from the current reading.

The cost of the electricity can be found using:

$$\text{cost} = \text{number of kilowatt-hours} \times \text{cost per kilowatt-hour}$$

The cost per kilowatt-hour depends on the time of day and how the electricity is generated.

For example, a student irons with a 1400 W iron for 30 minutes. If electricity costs 9p per kilowatt-hour how much does it cost to use the iron?

$$\text{Energy used} = 1.4\,\text{kW} \times 0.5\,\text{h} = 0.7\,\text{kWh}$$
$$\text{Cost} = 0.7\,\text{kWh} \times 9\text{p} = 6.3\text{p}$$

Exam tip

Take care with units when making these sorts of calculations. Remember that a kilowatt-hour is a unit of energy.

Nuclear power

Nuclear power stations use uranium as their fuel. Uranium is a non-renewable resource.

Nuclear fuel waste contains **plutonium**. It is radioactive and can be used to make nuclear bombs.

Advantages of nuclear power	Disadvantages of nuclear power
current uranium stocks are plentiful	high cost of building, maintaining and decommissioning nuclear power stations
does not rely on fossil fuels which are running out	risk of a serious accident releasing **radioactive material** into the atmosphere
does not produce carbon dioxide or contribute to global warming	transport, storage and disposal of radioactive nuclear waste is difficult and expensive

How science works

Nuclear power stations produce waste which can remain radioactive for thousands of years. This means that their use now produces waste that future generations will have to deal with.

Who do you think should decide whether or not to build nuclear power stations?

Test yourself

1 Give three advantages of using fossils fuels in power stations to generate electricity.

2 Calculate the current drawn from the 230 V mains supply by a kettle of power 1800 W.

3 Calculate the cost of using a 2300 W heater for 90 minutes if electricity costs 7p per kilowatt-hour.

4 A kettle of power 1500 W takes 6 minutes to boil when full. Each kilowatt-hour costs 10p. Calculate the cost of boiling the kettle.

5 Describe how uranium is used in a nuclear power station to generate electricity.

P2d Nuclear radiations

After revising this item you should:

- recall the three nuclear radiations and some of their uses, describe how to handle them safely and explain the problems of dealing with radioactive waste.

Nuclear radiation

Some materials give out **nuclear radiation** from the nuclei of their atoms. These are called radioactive materials. The three types of nuclear radiation are:

- **alpha** particles
- **beta** particles
- **gamma** rays

Ionisation

When nuclear radiations travel through a material they are able to knock electrons off the atoms causing other particles to gain electrons; this produces particles called ions. We call the process **ionisation**. The more ionisation that takes place the more quickly the energy of the nuclear radiation is used up, so the less distance it will penetrate into the material.

alpha particles	• the most ionising • the least penetrating • stopped by a few centimetres of air • stopped by a thin sheet of paper
beta particles	• less ionising than alpha but more ionising than gamma • more penetrating than alpha but less penetrating than gamma • stopped by a few metres of air • stopped by a thin sheet of metal
gamma rays	• the least ionising • the most penetrating • partially absorbed by several metres of concrete • partially absorbed by several centimetres of lead

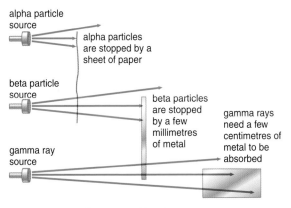

alpha particle source

alpha particles are stopped by a sheet of paper

beta particle source

beta particles are stopped by a few millimetres of metal

gamma rays need a few centimetres of metal to be absorbed

gamma ray source

Uses of nuclear radiation

Alpha particles are used:

- in smoke detectors. They cause ionisation of the air in the detector so that it conducts electricity and a small current flows. Smoke absorbs the alpha particles, the current is reduced and the alarm sounds.

Beta particles are used:

- by manufacturers of paper. The source is placed on one side of a continuous sheet of paper and a detector on the other. Changes to the thickness of the paper cause a change in the count rate detected.
- as tracers in medicine to allow doctors to monitor parts of the body without the need for surgery.

Gamma rays are used:

- to treat cancers. Beams of gamma rays from a source outside the body can kill tumour cells inside the body without the need for surgery.
- to kill bacteria on hospital equipment, sterilising it without the need for heating
- for non-destructive testing of welds in metals. If a gamma source is placed on one side of the weld and a photographic film on the other, any weak points in the weld will show up on the film.

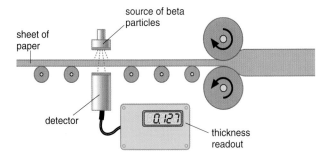

sheet of paper

source of beta particles

detector

0.127

thickness readout

How science works

Gamma radiation can be used to kill bacteria in food such as fruit and vegetables. This stops it rotting so the fruit lasts longer, although it may taste different.

Some people object to this; they may think that it makes their food radioactive.

Should food be labelled so that people know if it has been treated?

Hazards of nuclear radiation

All nuclear radiations can be harmful to people. They cause ionisation in living cells. This may result in the cell undergoing cancerous changes or being killed.

Radioactive materials must be handled safely.

- Sources of radiation should be handled with tongs and kept away from the body.
- Exposure times should be kept as short as possible.
- People who work with nuclear radiation should wear film badges to monitor their exposure.
- Gloves and protective clothing should be worn.
- Sources must be stored safely, in clearly labelled, shielded containers.

Background radiation

Background radiation is radiation that is around us all the time. It is caused by radioactive substances in rocks, soil and living things and **cosmic rays** from outer space.

Disposing of radioactive waste

We can dispose of **radioactive waste**, such as from a nuclear power station, in a number of ways.

- Low level waste can be buried in landfill sites.
- High level waste can be encased in glass and stored underground.
- Some of the waste can be reprocessed to make new fuel.

The waste is a big problem because:

- it emits harmful nuclear radiation
- some of the waste will remain radioactive for thousands of years
- there is always a risk that terrorists may use the waste to make nuclear bombs
- the waste cannot be allowed to enter groundwater supplies
- the level of radioactivity that is acceptable may change over time.

Test yourself

1 Why is using an alpha source in a smoke alarm not dangerous to people?

2 Why is beta radiation used to monitor paper thickness rather than alpha or gamma?

3 What is meant by ionisation?

4 Suggest why gamma rays are the most dangerous type of radiation outside the body.

5 Suggest why alpha particles are the most dangerous source of radiation inside the body.

P2e Our magnetic field & P2f Exploring our Solar System

After revising these items you should:

- be able to explain how scientists think the Earth's magnetic field comes about, describe our Solar System and explain the advantages and disadvantages of different types of space flight.

Magnetic fields

A magnetic field is a region where magnetic materials (such as iron and steel) will experience a force.

A plotting compass shows the direction of a magnetic field. All magnets have a north and a south pole. The Earth is surrounded by a magnetic field and this field has a north and a south pole.

A current is a flow of charged particles. An electric current in a coil of wire creates a magnetic field.

The shape of the Earth's magnetic field is like the shape of the one around a coil of wire when it is carrying a current.

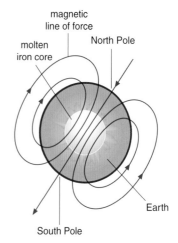

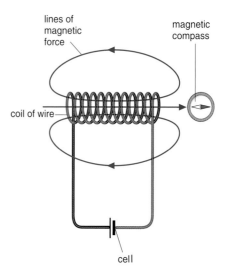

The core of the Earth contains a lot of molten iron. Scientists think that the magnetic field is made by large electric currents set up in the core as the Earth spins on its axis.

Cosmic rays

Cosmic rays are fast moving particles from outer space. When they hit the upper atmosphere they cause the production of gamma rays. Gamma rays may ionise materials that they pass through, so they can damage living organisms, causing cancer.

As the cosmic rays are charged, they are deflected by the Earth's magnetic field. They spiral around the lines of the Earth's magnetic field to the poles. The Aurora Borealis, or Northern Lights, seen in the night sky near the North Pole is caused by these cosmic rays.

Formation of the Moon

Scientists think that the Moon may be the result of a collision between the Earth and a large planet, billions of years ago.

- The two planets collided.
- The heavy iron from the cores of both planets merged to create the Earth.
- Less dense material merged to form the Moon.
- The Moon now orbits the Earth.

We can summarise the evidence for their ideas like this:

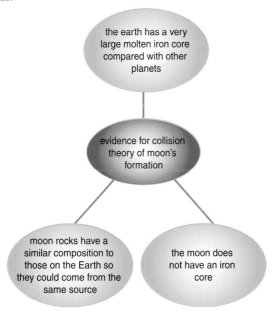

Solar flares

Solar flares:

- are clouds of charged particles ejected at high speed from the Sun
- create strong magnetic fields
- have sufficient energy to destroy the electronic circuits in orbiting satellites if the flares get close enough to the Earth
- produce surges of magnetism which can cause pulses of current to flow in large metal loops, such as those formed by electricity distribution networks. This can burn out transformers cutting off the supply.

The Solar System

The Earth is one of the **planets** that orbit the Sun and together form the Solar System. The closer the planet the shorter the orbit time. Mercury is the planet closest to the Sun. The order of the planets is Mercury, Venus, Earth, Mars, Jupiter, Saturn, Uranus, Neptune and Pluto.

How science works

Astronomers are discovering more and more objects in the far reaches of our Solar System. This meant that a new definition of a planet was needed.

In 2006, the International Astronomical Union agreed to reclassify Pluto as a 'dwarf planet' as it is part of an asteroid belt.

Many astronomers opposed this decision and the debate continues.

Anything moving in a circle requires a **centripetal force** towards the centre of the circle. Gravitational force provides the centripetal force that keeps the planets in orbit around the Sun, and the Moon in orbit around the Earth.

The Universe and space travel

The Universe consists of billions of **stars**. Large groups of stars are called galaxies. The Universe also contains **comets**, meteors and **black holes**.

To explore other parts of the solar system and beyond we need to send out **spacecraft**.

There are many difficulties associated with sending people into space in manned spacecraft, such as providing enough:

- food and water • oxygen • warmth • fuel

Using unmanned spacecraft has several advantages:

- They do not need water, food or oxygen.
- They do not put the health of humans at risk.
- They can withstand conditions that would kill humans.

But there is no-one onboard to carry out maintenance during a mission.

Unmanned spacecraft can be used to give us information about other planets, including:

- temperature, magnetism and radiation
- gravity and atmosphere.

Because of the vast distances involved, even electro-magnetic radiation such as light and radio waves takes a long time to travel though the Solar System.

A **light-year** is the distance light travels in a year. It is used as the unit of measurement for the very large distances in space.

How science works

The low gravity experienced in space is very bad for human health. Without the stress of walking, running and jumping the bones rapidly lose mass and become liable to breakage.

Scientists are looking for ways to overcome this problem by producing artificial gravity to mimic conditions on Earth.

Test yourself

1 Draw a sketch to show the shape of the magnetic field around a coil of wire carrying a current.

2 Describe how some scientists think the Moon may have been formed. Suggest why they cannot be certain their ideas are correct.

3 Describe three uses of artificial satellites.

4 Why are we able to see the planets even though they do not give out light?

5 Suggest why an unmanned spacecraft would cost less to use than a manned spacecraft for the same mission.

P2g Threats to Earth & P2h The Big Bang

After revising these items you should:

- know the difference between an asteroid and a comet, explain the evidence for the Big Bang theory and describe the life cycle of a star.

Asteroids

Asteroids are large rocks left over from the formation of the Solar System. Many of them orbit the Sun in the asteroid belt, between Mars and Jupiter. The belt is there because the huge gravitational pull of Jupiter stops the rocks joining together to form planets.

There are several pieces of evidence that large asteroids have collided with the Earth:

- Impact **craters** in the surface of the Earth.
- Layers of unusual elements, such as iridium, in rocks
- Sudden changes in the number of fossils in layers of rock that are next to each other, showing that the number of living creatures dropped suddenly.

Exam tip

Make sure you can explain the evidence that shows that large asteroids have collided with the Earth in the past.

Comets

Comets are balls of ice and dust that slowly orbit the Sun in large **elliptical** orbits far beyond the planets. The comet spends most of its time away from the Sun, but when it is close to the Sun it speeds up. Heat from the Sun melts the ice and a trail of debris forms a tail on the comet.

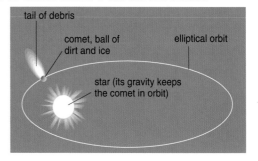

Near-Earth Object (NEOs)

A **Near-Earth Object** is an asteroid or a comet on a collision course with Earth – it would cause enormous damage if it hit.

Astronomers search for NEOs with telescopes. They can track their paths with satellites and try to work out their trajectories. This is difficult, as the path of a NEO can be changed by the gravitational pull of another planet. If scientists thought that an NEO was likely to collide with Earth it is possible that causing an explosion nearby could deflect its path.

How science works

Scientists in the USA track the path of large asteroids in the northern hemisphere. If they find one on a collision course with Earth they will have to make a choice: should they warn people and risk causing panic or would it be better for the public not to know.

What do you think?

The origin of the Universe

The stars are grouped together in galaxies, each containing about a billion stars. Light from distant galaxies is shifted towards the red end of the spectrum. The further away the galaxy the bigger the red shift. This shows that all galaxies are moving away from us, and the distant galaxies are moving away quickest. This is true in every direction and suggests that the whole Universe is expanding outwards.

If the Universe is expanding it leads to the conclusion that it must have started with an explosion from a small initial point, or Big Bang. This is what we call the **Big Bang theory**.

The theory is supported because the Universe is filled with microwave radiation. Immediately after the Big Bang, the Universe was filled with very short wavelength gamma radiation. As the Universe cooled this became long wavelength microwave radiation.

We think that the Universe came into existence about 15 billion years ago.

The life cycle of stars

Exam tip

Look at the diagram below. To help you learn the life cycle of a star make a sketch to show each stage.

How science works

Optical telescopes collect light. Other telescopes collect electromagnetic waves from different parts of the spectrum, from gamma rays to radio waves. Scientists use information from all parts of the electromagnetic spectrum to develop their ideas about the Universe.

Test yourself

1 Describe the difference between an asteroid and a comet.

2 What evidence is there to suggest that large asteroids may have collided with the Earth in the past?

3 Describe one piece of evidence for the Big Bang theory.

4 Why is a black hole black?

5 Describe the stages in the life cycle of a star much bigger than the Sun.

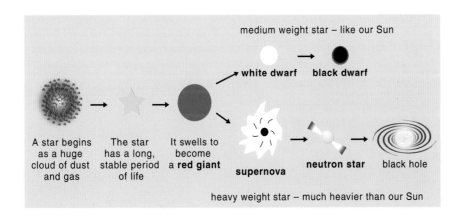

medium weight star – like our Sun

white dwarf → black dwarf

A star begins as a huge cloud of dust and gas → The star has a long, stable period of life → It swells to become a **red giant**

supernova → **neutron star** → black hole

heavy weight star – much heavier than our Sun

Exam-style questions

1 Cystic fibrosis is caused by a recessive allele, carried by about one person in 20. Only a person with two recessive alleles has the disorder. The recessive allele is represented by **f**.

(a) What is the probability of two carriers having a child that has the disorder?

....[1]

(b) What is the probability of two carriers having a child that is a carrier?

....[1]

(c) What is the genotype of someone with the disorder?

....[1]

(d) What is the genotype of a carrier?

....[1]

(e) Some diseases are caused by mutations. Mutation can be caused by many different things. Write down three of these things.

....

....

....[3]

2 Plants live in all parts of the world.

(a) Explain **two** ways in which a plant is adapted to live in hot dry places.

....

....[2]

(b) A plant has colourful petals. How is it pollinated?

....[1]

(c) Give an advantage of a plant having small, light pollen.

....[1]

(d) Plants make their own food by photosynthesis. Write down the products of photosynthesis and state how they are used by the plant.

....

....

....[3]

3 Polystyrene is an addition polymer.

(a) Explain what is meant by the term **addition polymer**.

....

....[2]

(b) The diagram shows part of the displayed formula of polystyrene.

$$
\begin{array}{cccccc}
H & C_6H_5 & H & C_6H_5 & H & C_6H_5 \\
| & | & | & | & | & | \\
-C- & C- & C- & C- & C- & C- \\
| & | & | & | & | & | \\
H & H & H & H & H & H
\end{array}
$$

Draw the displayed formula of the monomer from which polystyrene is made.

[2]

(c) Polystyrene is used in the packing of electrical goods to prevent damage in transit. What property of polystyrene makes it a good choice for this use?

....[1]

(d) Polystyrene has a fairly low melting point. Some other polymers have much higher melting points. Explain this difference. Use ideas about forces between polymer molecules.

....

....

....[3]

4 Along the western coast of South America an oceanic plate is colliding with and sliding beneath a continental plate.

(a) **(i)** What name is given to this process?

....[1]

(ii) What does this process show about the density of these plates?

....[1]

(iii) Explain what causes tectonic plates to move. A diagram may help you.

....
....[2]

(b) The western coast of South America is an area of volcanic activity. Lava released from volcanoes forms igneous rocks.

(i) Some igneous rocks have large crystals whilst others have small crystals.

Explain this difference.

....
....[2]

(ii) Geologists study volcanoes. Who may benefit from this study?

Explain why.

....
....[2]

5 Samir and Mena are going on a picnic. They plan to take some cold bottles of drink with them.

(a) Samir and Mena make a box to keep the bottles of drink cold. They make the box from expanded polystyrene covered in a layer of aluminium foil. The polystyrene contains many tiny air bubbles.

(i) Suggest why they made the box from expanded polystyrene.

....
....
....[3]

(ii) Suggest why they covered the box in aluminium foil.

....[1]

(b) They put 'freezer packs' into the box to help keep the bottles of drink cold. A freezer pack is a thick polythene bag containing a liquid. If the liquid is left in a freezer at −20°C overnight it turns into a solid.

(i) Explain how the freezer packs help to keep the bottles of drink cold.

....
....[2]

(ii) The table gives some information about three liquids.

Liquid	Melting point (°C)	Specific latent heat of fusion (J/kg)
ethanol	−114	109 000
salt water	−12	333 000
cyclohexane	7	39 000

Why is salt water used, rather than the other liquids, in the freezer packs?

Use the table to help you.

....
....[2]

6 (a) (i) Describe how electricity is generated at a coal-fired power station.

....
....
....
....[3]

(ii) Electricity from a power station is transmitted across the country using the National Grid. Explain why transformers are used to increase the voltage before transmission.

....
....
....[3]

(b) A hairdryer is connected to the 230 V mains supply. It uses a current of 6 A.

(i) Calculate the power of the hairdryer in kilowatts. Use the equation.

power = voltage × current

[2]

(ii) The hairdryer is used for 15 minutes. Calculate the cost of the electrical energy supplied if 1 kWh costs 9p.

[2]

Answers to exam-style questions

1 (a) 1 in 4 / 25% [1]

(b) 1 in 2 / 50% [1]

(c) ff [1]

(d) Ff [1]

(e) Any **three** from: UV light / Chemicals in the environment / Chemicals in cigarette smoke / Background radiation [3]

2 (a) Any **two** from: Long roots to reach water / Green stem for photosynthesis / Leaves reduced to spines to prevent water loss / Thick cuticle to prevent water loss / Reduced surface area to volume ratio to reduce water loss [2]

(b) By insects [1]

(c) The pollen can be blown easily by the wind [1]

(d) Glucose and oxygen; Glucose and oxygen are used in respiration; Glucose is stored as starch / changed into cellulose for cell walls [3]

3 (a) Large molecules made by adding together small molecules; With no other product [2]

(b) A diagram showing two carbon atoms joined by a double bond; Three hydrogen atoms and one C_6H_5 group joined to the carbon atoms [2]

(c) Hard / strong [1]

(d) Melting point depends on the forces of attraction between molecules / chains; Polystyrene has weak forces; Other polymers have stronger crosslinking [3]

4 (a) (i) Subduction [1]

(ii) Oceanic plates are denser than continental plates [1]

(iii) Convection currents; In the magma [2]

(b) (i) Slow cooling below ground forms large crystals; Rapid cooling above ground forms small crystals [2]

(ii) People living near active volcanoes; They may get early warning of an eruption [2]

5 (a) (i) Expanded polystyrene contains many trapped air bubbles; Air is a poor conductor; So the contents stay cool [3]

(ii) Aluminium foil reflects infrared [1]

(b) (i) Heat energy flows from the box to the freezer packs; The energy is used to melt the freezer packs [2]

(ii) The freezer is not cold enough to freeze ethanol; Salt water has a higher specific latent heat than cyclohexane so more energy is taken from the surroundings to melt it [2]

6 (a) (i) Coal is burned to produce heat which heats water; The water turns to steam which drives a turbine; The turbine drives a generator, producing electricity [3]

(ii) Increasing the voltage decreases the current; Lower current means less heating of the cables; This reduces wastage of energy [3]

(b) (i) Power = 6A × 230V; Power = 1380W = 1.38kW [2]

(ii) Electrical energy = 1.38kW × 0.25 hours = 0.345kWh; Cost = 0.345 × 9p = 3.1p [2]

Index of key words